# Warships
# and Navies
# Review

Edited by
Anthony J. Watts

LONDON

IAN ALLAN LTD

First published 1974

ISBN 0 7110 0496 X

Published by Ian Allan Ltd, Shepperton, Surrey
and printed in the United Kingdom by
A. Wheaton & Co, Exeter

*Title page:* A Soviet 'H–11' submarine. /*MoD, RN
Official*

*Above left:* Ships of the NATO Standing Naval
Force in the Mediterranean. The vessels are from
top to bottom: *Braunschweig, Evertsen, Aurora,
Charles F. Adams, Thermistocles* and *Izmir.*
/*Courtesy Commodore Fieldhouse*

*Above:* 'Close Quarters'. The Portuguese frigate
*Alimarante Pereira da Silva* and beyond the German
*Schleswig Holstein,* Dutch *Amsterdam* and *USS
Bigelow.* /*Courtesy Commodore Fieldhouse*

# Contents

5  Introduction
7  American Sea Power    *James D. Hessman*
23  The Soviet Underwater Threat    *Anthony J. Watts*
43  Nuclear Frigates of the United States Navy    *Anthony J. Watts*
46  The Balance of Power in the Mediterranean    *John Marriott*
58  The Royal Navy in Alliance    *Desmond Wettern*
67  The German Federal Navy    *Vice-Admiral F. Ruge*
79  Twenty Years of American Naval Guided Missiles    *S. Terzibaschitch*
88  Naval Surface-to-Air Guided Missiles    *Anthony J. Watts*

HMS *Ark Royal*.

# Introduction

In this second edition of *Warships & Navies* I have endeavoured to project an international outlook, covering those fields which seem to have attained major prominence over the last few years. Continuing the policy laid down in the introduction to the 1973 edition, this edition covers such widely varying topics as the present state of the American Navy and its future lines of development, the development of the Russian submarine and submarine strategy, various naval alliances and missile development. The two articles on the American and Russian Navies form the major part of *Warships & Navies Review*. I have dealt at some length with these two subjects for Russia and America are the two super powers in the world with large, powerful navies, and have opposing ideologies which could, if the political situation ever deteriorated to such an extent, bring these two mighty nations into conflict. I feel it is important, therefore, to examine in detail certain aspects of the naval potential of these two countries.

At present the American Navy is going through a great period of change. The Vietnam War is at long last over and many lessons will have been learnt and many new ideas resulting from action in this bitter war will have to be carefully studied and absorbed in order to make a correct assessment of future American naval requirements. At the same time much of the strength of the American Fleet is vested in vessels of World War II vintage and just after; vessels which have now reached the end of their useful life, a life which no amount of modernising and rebuilding can rejuvenate. It is essential to replace these units, but there are so many conflicting needs, and America, like many other countries, is now fighting raging inflation, which does nothing to alleviate the problems of the Navy. For cost reasons alone it would be impossible to realise all the plans and programmes which have been put forward. The dilemma facing the Americans is to decide which of these programmes is most vital for the defence of America, and which can either be abandoned or delayed until sufficient money can safely be made available to implement them. Many of the ideas, as explained in the article, are revolutionary and will cost billions to develop.

The problem facing the Russian Navy is slightly different. Here money is no object, but developing satisfactory weapons systems does seem at times to present the Russians with grave problems. The greatest threat the West faces is that of the Russian submarine fleet, which on paper is the largest and possibly the most deadliest in the world. But is it as powerful as it seems, or is it only a 'Paper Tiger'? It is true that by sheer weight of numbers alone the Russian submarine Fleet could overwhelm Western A/S defences, and break through to wreak havoc among the merchant shipping routes and threaten our cities and industrial centres with POLARIS missiles. However, the total strength of the Russian submarine arm is divided among four major fleets in widely scattered parts of the world. Herein lies both its strength, and its weakness; for as the article describes Russian warship design has nearly always lagged behind that of the West by at least two or three years and so their fleet, although largely built within the last 20 years, would not always be capable of penetrating the West's small but highly efficient A/S defences. Many of the Russian submarines are now obsolete and individually could not hope to break through our defence cordon, but they could succeed by use of large numbers, if these could be assembled at the right time and in the right place. The Russians may be forced to disperse their submarines between four fleets but this in turn means that the West is forced to disperse its A/S vessels around the globe to meet this threat. It is the old problem encountered during World War II when one lightly armed German merchant raider could tie down dozens of warships searching for it. With no fixed limit on defence expenditure Russia is always prepared to make up what she lacks for in quality in her armed forces by resorting to numbers, believing that the end result certainly

justifies the means, even if this entails high losses in the process. There is also an enigma surrounding the way the Russian submarine arm would be controlled in time of war, and as the article shows, her past performances in the field of submarine strategy have by no means been brilliant.

America alone cannot shoulder responsibility for defence of the west, and to help provide a fully co-ordinated defence it has been policy for some years now to exercise continuously throughout the year, in a fully integrated command, various types of warship from the member countries of NATO. Britain's role in similar areas of co-operation is outlined in this edition.

At present one of the most sensitive spots in the world is the Mediterranean. Here vessels of the Russian navy are in almost daily confrontation with units of the American Sixth Fleet and vessels of the French and Italian Navies. Where does the balance of power in the Mediterranean lie? This is a question of vital importance to the whole world, for if the West once loses control of this area then the way lies open for Russia to completely dominate Southern Europe, North Africa and the Western Approaches of the Atlantic, an area vital to the defence of Northern Europe and Great Britain.

A navy which is taking an increasing share in the defence of Europe through its membership to NATO is the German Federal Navy. Since World War II this navy has grown into a well balanced and co-ordinated force capable of undertaking defence of its own

'Kashin' class guided missile destroyer at Ethiopian Navy Days. Note the launchers for GOA surface-to-air missiles fore and aft and associated fire control and tracking radar (Cheapside and Peel Group)./*MoD, RN, Official*

coastline and providing a vital contribution to the Western Alliance. The article on the German Navy describes its growth since the last war and its future plans for expansion.

On the technical side one of the most vital forms of defence is undertaken by the guided missile. For many years America has led the world in missile development, and the article on American naval missiles traces these developments and describes many of the vessels now equipped with guided weapons.

Finally, with the certainty that Russia is now building a large carrier and developing a V/STOL aircraft to operate from the vessel, it is pertinent to examine the naval surface-to-air missile systems at present in use or under development by the various navies in the world. The article concludes with a table giving comparisons of the various major features of these missiles.

As stated in the 1973 edition there is always the possibility that material may become outdated. All the facts quoted within the articles were, as far as is known, correct at the time of going to press.

A.J.W.

*The opinions expressed in the articles are those of the writers and not necessarily those of any official body.*

# American Sea Power

## JAMES D. HESSMAN

As American Navy leaders ponder how to stretch limited resources to cover seemingly infinite requirements in building a new post-Vietnam fleet which could serve as the nation's first line of defence for the remainder of the century, they face numerous extremely difficult, if not insoluble, problems.

Most of these fall into three broad and, of course, constantly overlapping areas–personnel, hardware, and politics – which together form the tripod upon which the future Navy is to be built. And the Navy, as well as the Administration which it serves, cannot afford to concentrate on any one area to the neglect of the others; kick any leg of a tripod and the whole structure collapses, no matter how sound or sturdy the other two legs.

On the personnel side the most immediate problems involve the end of the Selective Service System, or draft, and its effect on the Navy, the outbreak of racial conflicts on board many ships (a problem which seems likely to continue), maintenance of discipline and readiness in what some view as a too permissive military climate, and the decision to assign women to sea duty – a decision with implications far more serious than would appear at first blush.

The Navy's hardware problems are more tangible, but no less difficult, and boil down to this: the United States Navy was, at the end of 1972, still by far the most powerful in the entire world, but its margin of superiority was rapidly slipping. Already the Soviet Navy had in commission more submarines and, more important, would soon have deployed a larger number of ballistic missile submarines. The Soviet Navy is newer and more austere, is equipped with a variety of anti-ship missiles against which the West has as yet no adequate defence, and seems bent on becoming air capable. The American Navy on the other hand, is considerably older, somewhat battle-scarred, possibly too habitability conscious, and much over-committed. A number of exciting and marvelously capable new ships, helicopters and fixed wing aircraft are on the drawing boards, to be sure, but the Navy simply will not have the money to buy all it needs of each, so will have to make some painful economic choices and accept whatever risks such choices entail.

In the political arena, which ultimately will be the crucial battleground, the Navy must first sell its programmes within the Administration and then to the United States Congress, which has become increasingly testy of late – but with good reason. The nation is war weary, alarmed about inflation – and anxious, therefore, to cut government spending (which means, in effect, cutting military spending) – and somewhat ambivalent about future relationships with both allies and enemies.

### The Nixon Doctrine

Before the Navy can come to grips with its more parochial problems, of course, the nation as a whole must first decide, through its elected representatives, what national security policy it wishes to pursue for the foreseeable future. Or, stated another way, how much security it is willing to pay for. No responsible official in either major national party has even admitted, or is ever likely to admit, that the United States could make do with anything less than a military establishment 'second to none'. It is only when terms are defined – what type of, and how many, ships, aircraft, tanks, etc, constitute the necessary minimum – and price tags are looked at, that the arguments start.

The parameters of future American national security policy were laid out in the summer of 1969 in what was originally known as the 'Guam Doctrine' but is now generally referred to as the 'Nixon Doctrine'. The broad policy guidelines spelled out in the Nixon Doctrine were translated by former (1969–73) American Defence Secretary Melvin R. Laird into what he terms a "National Security Strategy of Realistic Deterrence". It is probable that future administrations will change the name,

7

but it matters little, because the guidelines likely will remain the same. When semantics have been stripped away the 'Nixon Doctrine' and Realistic Deterrence Strategy boil down to several key points:

(a) The United States will maintain a strong nuclear deterrent, and will conduct itself so as to leave no doubt as to the credibility of that deterrent.

(b) The United States will maintain its treaty commitments (but probably not undertake any new ones).

(c) The United States will expect other parties to regional security alliances to provide maximum commitment of their own manpower and material resources for their own defence before asking the United States to come to the rescue.

(d) When American help *is* needed, it will probably come in the form of military assistance (weapons, money, foodstuffs, ammunition, and other supplies), rather than troops. White House and Pentagon officials obviously want to avoid another Vietnam – but they have never unequivocally renounced the future use of American troops, ships, and/or aircraft in overseas conflicts vital to American interests.

(e) Preventive maintenance will be stressed; ie, the United States will strive through diplomatic channels (the United Nations, preferably) to prevent conflicts before they start – acting as honest broker, for example, in developing a new rapprochement between the Arabs and Israelis.

(f) Perhaps most important of all, the United States will do everything in its power short of surrender to bring about an end to the Cold War, improvement of relations between NATO and the Warsaw Pact, and development of economic, cultural, and other non-military ties between the two superpowers and their respective military allies.

Such lofty principles are more easily enunciated than put into practice, of course, but the Nixon Administration seems to have been relatively consistent in following its own foreign policy and national security guidelines. The so-called Vietnamisation pro-gramme, for example, is convincing evidence that American manpower may never again be committed to fight 'other people's battles' –although United States material assistance apparently will be generously supplied to those allies who are willing, in fact, to 'fight their own fights'.

Similarly, the SALT Agreements, the Nixon visits to Peking and Moscow, the Laird 'burden-sharing' lectures to NATO allies, and the numerous behind-the-scenes efforts to defuse the Middle East all had the same objectives: to reduce the incidence of military conflicts throughout the world, to avoid entirely, or at least reduce, the extent of American and NATO involvement in those conflicts which do occur, and to encourage proportionately equal effort and sacrifice on the part of the United States and its allies when involvement is unavoidable.

## A Bigger Role for the Navy

Army and Air Force partisans don't like to admit it, but the 'Nixon Doctrine' upgrades the Navy somewhat at the expense of the other United States services – all of which played a bigger role in the Vietnam fighting. The Air Force, with its MINUTEMAN missiles and long range bombers, still has two-thirds ownership of the nuclear deterrent 'triad', with the Navy's POLARIS/POSEIDON (and, later, TRIDENT) fleet constituting the other third. The Army is being upgraded in quality, but its numbers have been cut considerably – from a Vietnam peak of 1,570,343 to an estimated on-board count of 828,000 in mid-1973. The Marine Corps – technically in the Navy Department but for most practical purposes operating as a separate service – will probably remain the same, with 200,000 men or so on the roster. It is of interest, incidentally, that the Marine Corps is the only American service which, to date, anyway, has come out of each conflict in which the United States has been involved bigger than when it went in.

If the theory of a bigger Navy role was not convincing evidence that the 'Nixon Doctrine' is basically – in military terms, at least – an oceanic strategy, then the Defence Department budget certainly proved this fact. For two consecutive years the Navy has been given the 'biggest third' ($24.9billion in fiscal 1973), with Army and Air Force shares steadily dropping ($20.9billion and $23.7 billion, respectively), and Navy predominance was expected to continue with the fiscal 1974 budget which, if the precedent of the past six or seven years is followed, a leisurely Congress will not give final approval to until November or December 1973 – five or six months after the fiscal year has started.

It is in the Congress, in fact, that the Navy – and, indeed, the entire American defence establishment – will face its greatest hurdle. Despite the overwhelming magnitude of the McGovern defeat in the 1972 American presidential elections, there seems little doubt that the 93rd Congress will prove a bit more liberal than its predecessor. Being more liberal does not, of course, mean being 'anti-military', but in recent years that is the way it has worked out.

Congress has actually cut Defence Department budgets very little in recent years – and virtually all cuts that have been made have been accomplished within the hallowed confines of the House and Senate Armed Services Committees and Defence Appropriations Sub-committees, four panels which in the mythology of the mass media are little more than rubber stamps for military budget requests.

But if the Congressional anti-military bloc (which say it isn't anti-military at all; it merely is convinced less military strength will still be enough) hasn't succeeded in its frontal attacks on numerous weapons programmes, it has succeeded in another way, by forcing a nervous Pentagon to take a long hard look at new programmes, to insist on more frugal management of continuing programmes, and to make large budget cuts in-house before submitting borderline items to Capitol Hill.

Even so, the fiscal 1974 Defence budget, submitted to Congress in late January 1973, had come under attack from the Congressional anti-military bloc even before the ink was dry on its pages. Legislators, mostly on the liberal side, offered a variety of arguments – some persuasive, some not – seeking to develop a large enough coalition to force through truly substantial cuts in the Defence budget (with the ultimate end of using the money thus 'saved' for domestic programmes of a presumably higher priority).

Because the debate will continue for years, and because NATO as well as the American Navy and overall United States national security interests are involved, it would seem in order, before taking a closer look at specific Navy programmes, to briefly review some of the more plausible and more persistent arguments (and Pentagon/Administration rebuttals thereof) advanced by the budget-cutters:

(1) The Vietnam War, which was costing the United States over $25billion annually at its peak, has ended. Overall United States military expenditure should be reduced, therefore, by at least $25billion per year, Pentagon spokesmen, led by Laird – who during his four years at the Defence Department helm proved more credible *and* more knowledgeable than his various 'loyal opposition' opponents – point out, and they have the figures to prove it, that inflation and frequent military pay raises (nine in the 1964–72 period) have already eaten up any potential 'savings', and more. They also point out, quite truthfully, that outlays for Vietnam would have been appreciably higher had not the military absorbed much of the cost of the war by stretching out production runs of some weapons programmes, deferring or cancelling others, depleting previously accumulated stockpiles, postponing much needed force modernisation, and otherwise living 'off the shelf'. Lastly, they say, the budget-cutters' arguments are irrelevant in any case because Soviet technological advances in virtually every military area now make it mandatory that United States forces be upgraded and modernised.

(2) Relations are improving with the Soviet Union and Communist China. For this reason, and particularly in view of American balance of payments deficits, the United States can safely afford to reduce its European garrison. This is a favourite theme of Senate Majority Leader Mike Mansfield, a Montana Democrat who commands more respect than obedience, and it strikes a responsive chord

both with those worried about inflation and those who feel that the United States has been pulling too much of the NATO load too long, and with too little help and too little appreciation. The Administration position is that other NATO members have, in fact, increased their own military contributions to NATO in recent years (and are being pressed to take on an even greater share of the load in the future), and that, in any event, the threat to Western and, therefore, American interests has not diminished, despite the warming trend of recent events.* If relations with the Soviet Union continue to improve, and particularly if substantial economic ties develop, partial American troop withdrawals will almost certainly follow. Defence Department planners, realising this, now argue more about the timing, than about the fact of withdrawal. Unilateral United States action would be militarily and diplomatically foolish, they say; it would be better to delay and negotiate mutual American and Soviet force reductions (MBFR) on both sides of the Iron Curtain. Those who defend this rationale realise, of course, that MBFR would work out much better for Russia, whose troops could return to the European theatre much more quickly than United States-based American forces. (3) Because of inflation, huge cost 'overruns' on various weapons systems (of which more later), and the lack of money for various domestic programmes, the United States can no longer afford a large military establishment, and can finance only a limited number of the new hardware systems which United States military leaders say are needed. Defence officials say they agree with the philosophy of this argument, but quickly add that the American Services are already operating close to the bone, and warn that additional cuts could seriously jeopardise United States national security interests. As evidence of in-house frugality and economy they cite the fact that the post-Vietnam force will be 200,000 to 300,000 men lower than the pre-Vietnam establishment. Finally, they point out that most, if not all, questionable hardware programmes are eliminated at the

* See 'The Royal Navy in Alliance' by D. Wettern.

individual Service, Defence Department, or OMB (Office of Management and Budget) levels before being submitted to Congress for approval – even in the McNamara years, it is known, the collective Service-approved hardware 'shopping lists' usually ran some $20 billion per year higher than the total finally approved by the Defence Department and OMB for submission to Congress.

**The Zumwalt Approach**

Working within the confines of national strategic policy and political limitations described above, United States Navy leaders are now face to face with two unpleasantly contradictory facts of life: first, that Navy commitments are likely to increase and expand dramatically as the 'Nixon Doctrine' develops and transforms from theory into practice; and second, that the Navy will have fewer ships and less manpower to carry out its increased commitments – it will have to do more and more with less and less, in other words.

Putting first things first, Chief of Naval Operations, Admiral Elmo R. Zumwalt, Jr, soon after he took office ordered all ahead flank on a number of 'new initiatives' in ship programmes based on what he conceives to be the fourfold Navy mission of the future: (1) Maintenance of a credible 'second strike' seabased nuclear deterrent force; (2) Control of the sea – both shipping lanes and specific ocean areas; (3) Projection of seabased power ashore; and (4) Maintenance of an overseas presence in peacetime.

To accomplish these missions, as Zumwalt sees it (and other senior Navy officials seem to agree) the Navy needs, respectively: (1) To maintain the POLARIS/POSEIDON fleet at full strength, and begin now to develop a follow-on programme; (2) Strong ASW forces, including nuclear attack submarines, ASW carriers, and purpose-built destroyers, frigates, and smaller combatants; (3) Attack carriers, shore bombardment ships, and amphibious assault ships; and (4) Combatant ships of any type – the bigger the better and the more the better.

Realising he will not get everything he feels the Navy needs, Zumwalt pared down the

*Above:* Inflation and the rising cost of production of various weapons systems are as serious a menace to the American Navy as they are to the Royal Navy. When completed in 1965 the USS *America* (above) had cost the Government $248,800,000./*Official USN*

*Below:* The carrier CVN 70 will be the world's first billion dollar vessel. A sister ship to the *Dwight D. Eisenhower* (depicted here in an artist's sketch and herself expected to cost $616 m) she will be the third of the 'Nimitz' class and possibly the last carrier to be built by the American Navy./*Official USN*

'shopping list' above to an essential number of the new initiatives programmes, the most viable of which are (not necessarily in order of Zumwalt's priority): CVN-70, the new nuclear attack carrier; TRIDENT, originally called ULMS, or Underwater Long-range Missile System, the POLARIS/POSEIDON successor; the PF or Patrol Frigate; the SCS or Sea Control Ship, a 'mini-carrier' of sorts; the PHM or Guided Missile Hydrofoil Patrol Craft; and the SES, of Surface Effect Ship – in reality a revolutionary new system of propulsion adaptable for use throughout the fleet and holding promise of, in the words of Dr. Robert A. Frosch, former Assistant Secretary of the Navy for Research and Development, providing "a greater advancement in surface ship capabilities than any in the last century".

Not included in the above are a number of other important ship programmes inherited by Zumwalt from his predecessor, Admiral Thomas H. Moorer, now Chairman of the United States Joint Chiefs of Staff. Among these continuing programmes are the LHA multi-purpose amphibious assault ship, the DD-963 'Spruance'-class destroyer, POLARIS-to-POSEIDON conversions, the SSN-688 class nuclear attack submarine, the DLGN nuclear frigate, the DE-1052 'Knox'-class escort, and a replacement for 'carrier capable' AAW guided missile destroyers and frigates.

## Lost: One Combat Fleet

The above assortment seems more ambitious than it is in actuality, and represents nothing less than a desparate Navy attempt to recoup a sizable combat fleet lost not to enemy action but to inflation and Defence budget cuts in the late 1960s. According to tables provided for the Senate Armed Services Committee by Zumwalt during so-called 'authorisation' hearings on the fiscal 1973 Defence Department budget, Navy planners in 1967, looking eight years ahead, had programmed a 1975 combatant fleet of 826 ships. Included in that number would be 20 carriers, 137 amphibious assault ships, 243 escort ships, 69 nuclear attack submarines, and 36 conventional attack submarines.

In 1968 plans for the 1975 fleet were scaled down to 793 ships, including 21 carriers, 99 amphibious assault ships, 238 escorts, 68 nuclear attack submarines, and 37 conventional attack submarines.

A deeper cutback followed in 1969, when the putative 1975 force was further reduced – to 713 ships. In the new total were 20 carriers, 77 amphibious assault ships, 240 escorts, 69 nuclear attack submarines, and 38 conventional attack submarines.

The most unkindest cut of all came in 1970, when another 135 ships were lopped off the future inventory – bringing the total projected 1975 on-board count to 578 ships – which this time would include only 15 carriers, 67 amphibious assault vessels, 205 escorts, 68 nuclear attack submarines, and 19 conventional attack submarines.

From 1967 to 1970, as the authoritative *Armed Forces Journal* (an independently published United States military magazine) perceptively noted in its April 1972 issue, "the American Navy of the future had lost, in effect, five aircraft carriers, 70 amphibious assault ships, 38 escort ships, 18 attack submarines, and 117 other ships (248 ships in all, or 30 per cent of its originally projected 1975 fleet), and without one enemy shot having been fired!"

A large share of the numbers cutback, it is only fair to note, resulted from older-ship euthanasia decreed by Zumwalt himself. Defending the 'hard choices' he had to make in marking up the Navy's fiscal 1973 budget, the CNO told the Senate Armed Services Committee last year that the basic 'trade-offs' were "between the present and the future – that is, between spending heavily to provide a greater capability today by keeping more older ships in service, or using more funds to procure new ships and aircraft thereby increasing future capability".

Acknowledging that present American Navy strength is still adequate – but only barely – to cope with a constantly increasing Soviet oceanic threat, Zumwalt opted for the future: "(In) the budget we are requesting," he told the Committee, ". . . we have continued to emphasize the future. For the second straight year we are putting an increased proportion of our resources into future capabilities. . . . Unfortunately, this means fewer ships and aircraft in the fleet in the next few years."

A second type of trade-off, Zumwalt said, spelling out what has since become known as the 'hi-lo-mix,' involves choosing between a small number of individual ships and aircraft of "greater sophistication", and, therefore, higher unit costs, and "procuring greater numbers of less sophisticated, less expensive weapons".

Here then, briefly, are thumbnail sketches of the more important hard-choice ships for the Navy of the future which are now on the ways, on the drawing boards, or still being debated before Congress:

**CVN-70**: Not, in truth, one of the 'new initiatives' programmes, the big new nuclear carrier – the Navy's fourth, and third of the 'NIMITZ' class – will have the dubious distinction of becoming the world's first 'billion dollar ship'. Advance funding for the big flat-top was voted by Congress last year, but the bulk of construction money would be in the fiscal 1974 and 1975 budgets, and anti-carrier forces in Congress (with some help from Pentagon people who would prefer using carrier money for other programmes) were girding up for a last-ditch assault. The outlook on Capitol Hill is that CVN-70 will be funded but it will be a squeeze, and the Navy may never get another carrier.

Navy spokesmen say, incidentally, that there are no plans "at present" for any carriers beyond CVN-70, but over three years ago Congress was given documents indicating Navy intentions to bring CVAN-71 and CVAN-72 into the fleet in 1978 and 1980, respectively. These plans obviously have been scaled down, but there is a lurking suspicion the Navy will, in fact, press for additional nuclear carriers – smaller than CVN-70, however – later in the decade.

Plans for CVN-70, which, like its predecessors, would be built by the Newport News (Va.) Shipbuilding and Dry Dock Co, call for a ship 1,092 feet long, over 95,000 tons fully loaded, and capable of a sustained speed of over 30 knots with virtually unlimited range. Like *Nimitz* and *Dwight D. Eisenhower*,

CVN-70 will, presumably, be fitted with SEA SPARROW missiles and the BPDMS (Basic Point Defence Missile System). She will have a 3,300-man crew, plus 2,800 assigned to a multi-purpose air wing which would include, in one breakdown provided to Congress, 24 F-14 (Tomcat) fighters, 24 A-7 (Corsair) attack aircraft, 12 A-6 (Intruder) attack aircraft, four KA-6 (Intruder) tankers, three RA-5 (Vigilante) reconnaissance planes, four E-2 (Hawkeye) early warning aircraft, four EA-6 (Intruder) electronic warfare planes, 10 S-3 (Viking) ASW aircraft, and eight SH-3 (Sea King) helicopters.

Zumwalt told Congress he considers CVN-70 the "item of highest priority" in the Navy's budget, and said without it "we forego any prospect of assuring our naval superiority in the later 1970s and 1980s.*

**Trident**: Billed by the press as another possible 'billion dollar ship' – Navy officials say $750million is closer to the mark – TRIDENT should have an easier go in Congress than CVN-70. Few if any legislators actually oppose the programme, although some are urging a go-slow approach (for economic rather than military reasons) and others want to hold down the numbers.

Laird alarmed TRIDENT managers last year with a seemingly off-hand reference to a 10-ship TRIDENT fleet. Earlier plans were to build anywhere from 25 to 40 ships to replace the 41-ship POLARIS/POSEIDON fleet. A final count of 15–20 now seems likely, and would still give the future underseas deterrent force an awesome strike capability. Each ship will carry 20 or 24 missiles, and each of those would be MIRVed (fitted with Multiple Independently-targeted Re-entry Vehicles) to carry 10 to 20 warheads.

TRIDENT will be from 450 to 500 feet long, displace from 8,000 to 12,000 tons, and have a maximum firing range of about 6,000 miles, and will be able to operate, according to

* *Note:* A CVA is an attack carrier, a CVAN a nuclear attack carrier, a CVS an ASW carrier. CVs and CVNs are multi-purpose – attack and ASW combined – ships, proven feasible during a Mediterranean deployment by *Saratoga*. The Navy plans to redesignate *Enterprise* (CVAN-65) and possibly other carriers as CVNs.

earlier unclassified posture testimony (for some reason, later reports *are* classified), from an acean area of 55 million square miles. POLARIS ships are limited to a three million square mile operating area to stay within firing range of currently assigned potential targets.

**Patrol Frigate:** Once almost aborted – Congress killed a $51.6million Navy request for the PF programme in fiscal 1972 – the Patrol Frigate now seems viable, although the Navy may still have a hard time getting the number (50) it is seeking. The 3,400-ton (full load) 420-foot ship would carry HARPOON and STANDARD missiles to give it both anti-missile and anti-air capability. Mk 32 torpedoes, a LAMPS (Light Airborne Multi-Purpose System)* helicopter and 35mm anti-aircraft guns also are planned.

Current plans are to delay follow-on buys until construction of the lead ship is well under way, and then to accelerate deliveries by ordering series construction in three different yards.

The mission of the PF will be to escort amphibious forces, merchant ships, and underway replenishment groups (URGs). Its 'offensive ASW' capability will be used to keep the sea lanes open in areas of less-than-maximum threat. In another 'hard choice' compromise, Zumwalt told Congress, the Navy "consciously eliminated shore bombardment and ASW escort for fast carrier strike forces from its mission in order to keep the price down".

**Sea Control Ship** – Another ship tailored for principal use in limited threat areas, the SCS – earlier called the Air Capable Ship (ACS) or, in the British version, Through Deck Cruiser (TDC) – may be the poor man's answer to the billion-dollar carrier. According to *Jane's*, whose excellent American section is edited by the peerless Norman Polmar, the Sea Control Ship will be about 550 feet long, displace 15,000 tons, carry 14 helicopters (probably SH-3 Sea Kings) and three AV-8 Harrier V/STOL strike aircraft, be armed with the Vulcan/Phalanx 20mm Close-In Weapon System, and be capable of a 25 knot speed.

* See J. D. Brown's article on helicopters in *Warships & Navies 1973*.

The amphibious assault ship *Guam* has been tested as an interim SCS – *Guam* is 18,300 tons, 592 feet long, and 84 feet at the beam. Eight first generation SCS ships are planned at a cost (after the lead ship is funded) of less than $100million each. Full funding of the first ship or ships is planned for Fiscal 1974, with initial operational capability in 1978.

SCS missions will include anti-submarine and anti-air warfare, defence against anti-ship missiles, early warning, and surface attack.

**Guided Missile Hydrofoil Patrol Craft:** Funding of two PHMs in the fiscal 1973 budget launched what the Navy hopes will be an eventual 30-ship programme – with NATO funding of some of the later buys, however.

The PHM is an outgrowth of the earlier 58-ton hydrofoil gun boats (PGH) – *Tucumcari* and *Flagstaff* – built as competitive prototypes to test the hydrofoil principle. The larger 170-ton PHMs will be about 120 feet long and will be able to fly at foilborne speeds of over 40 knots. Planned armament will be the HARPOON Surface-to-surface missile and a 3in rapid-fire dual purpose gun. A standard NATO variant would have essentially the same hull, propulsion and foil systems as the American version but, at the user country's option, different weapons and command and control systems. The United States Navy's mission for the PHMs was spelled out for Congress as follows: "To operate offensively against major surface craft and to conduct surveillance, screening, and special operations". Translated, this means they will probably be used to 'shadow' Soviet ships and carry out other missions in restricted waters where their high speed and small size can be used to tactical advantage. The Baltic approaches, English Channel, and both ends of the Mediterreanean are likely bases of operation for the PHMs.

Navy planners estimate the two lead ships will cost $65.5million, but say that follow-on ships (United States version) can be kept to "less than $18million".

**Surface Effect Ship** (SES): The most exciting, the most revolutionary, but undoubtedly furthest down the line of all the new

*Above:* The USS *Guam* is at present undergoing trials to test the feasibility of plans for a new type of vessel for use in limited threat areas—the Sea Control Ship. The picture shows an AV-8A Harrier V/STOL aircraft preparing to land on the *Guam* while an H-46 Sea Knight helicopter in the foreground carries out plane guard duties./*Official USN*

*Right:* Plans are now being drawn up for a 30-ship guided missile hydrofoil patrol boat programme. After extensive trials with the hydrofoil gunboat *Tucumcari* (right) the concept of the hydrofoil as a weapons system has now been well and truly established./*Official USN*

*Above :* By far the most revolutionary design at present under consideration by the United States Navy is the Surface Effect Ship (SES). With an incredible speed of between 80 and 100 knots this type of craft could revolutionise naval warfare./*Official USN*

*Below :* The LHA is a multi-purpose amphibious warfare vessel, but its construction is well behind schedule and it is also suffering from high cost overruns./*Official USN*

initiatives programmes, the SES represents, in Zumwalt's words, "a technological break-through that offers the potential for revolutionizing naval warfare".

Principal characteristic of the SES, and the one which has so excited Navy and Defence Department planners, is its high speed – up to 180 knots in some studies, but with a 'best efficiency range' of somewhere between 80 and 100 knots.

Two 100-ton prototype SES craft built as testbeds for multithousand ton follow-ons have already demonstrated feasibility of the SES for smaller combatant roles – for which, however, as other tests have proven, hydrofoils are more efficient. The Navy in late 1972 awarded preliminary design contracts to four American firms (Aerojet General, Bell Aerospace, Litton, and Lockheed) to do preliminary designs of a 2,000-ton SES – which planners say is the smallest SES "likely to have military value in the deep ocean". Later versions, which may not be operational until the 1980s or 1990s, could go as high as 20,000 tons, according to present plans.

The SES achieves its spectacular speeds through the use of rigid sidewalls running fore and aft on either side of the ship and flaps or seals on the bow and stern which together provide a captured air bubble (CAB) on which the ship rides, just above the surface of the water. Propulsion will be by waterjet or supercavitating propellers. Studies have also been initiated to determine the feasibility of nuclear propulsion for SES vessels.

Many missions are planned for the SES ranging from ASW to carrier escort – the large economy size SES could itself serve as a unique type of 'mini-carrier', depending on its high speed to launch and recover aircraft on relatively short flight decks which would need no catapults or arresting gear. In its ASW configuration, of course, the SES would be able to outrun any torpedo launched against it and, depending on its own weapons suit, would have a much better than average survival chance against the cruise missile.

Of all the new initiatives, the SES also offers the most fascinating commercial possibilities. The SES research and development programme started, in fact, as a 50–50

partnership between the Navy and the United States Commerce Department, but the latter dropped out for 'lack of funds' – correctly judging, however, that the Navy would continue the programme in any case, as it has. Military applications will thus come first, but commercial use will not be far behind – passenger service and transport of perishables and high-value-per-ton cargoes are but two of many possible commercial uses for the SES, which would largely close the transportation gap between high-cost, extremely-fast air transportation and very-low-cost very-low-speed water transportation – the New York to Southampton run, for example, could be reduced to less than 30 hours.

**Amphibious Assault Ship:*** The multi-purpose LHA – designed to serve as a combination LPH (older type amphibious assault ship), LKA (amphibious cargo ship), and LPD (amphibious transport dock) – has run into money and time problems. Rather high cost overruns, combined with a programme slippage of 12–18 months or longer, have put Litton, the prime contractor, in the Navy's doghouse. The Navy, it is only fair to say, compounded the problem by reducing an earlier planned buy of 9 ships to 5 (a move in which American economic interests and the 'Nixon Doctrine' coincided quite nicely). The Marine Corps is not at all happy with the cut. United States contingency plans call for sufficient amphibious lift capability to support a Marine Amphibious Force (a Marine division and its accompanying air wing). The five LHAs planned will provide that capability but they will be split between two oceans.

When the LHAs are delivered they may be very late and too small, but the Navy and Marine Corps should have remarkably capable ships. Each LHA will be 820 feet long, 106 feet at the beam, about 40,000 tons fully loaded, and capable of a 22 knot sustained speed. Armament will consist of three 5in/54 guns, two Basic Point Defence Missile System launchers, troop helicopters, and, possibly, the Harrier. Flight deck, half-length hangar deck, and a docking well big enough to fit four LCU 1610 landing craft

* See also *Warships & Navies 1973* p. 48.

will give the LHA unique amphibious capabilities. The 1,825 man crew will include 163 officers and 1,662 enlisted men.

**SPRUANCE-Class Destroyer:** The DD-963 ships, Navy officials say, are "urgently needed" to replace destroyers now in the inventory – the latter ships will be 30 years old or so, a Methuselahan age for an ocean-going combatant, by the time the 'Spruance's' join the fleet. Litton is also building the DD-963s, and early reports indicate the programme will be late, due to the LHA slippage. Costs so far seem to have been kept under better control, but the combination of cost plus slippage could induce Congress to reduce the 30-ship buy originally planned. The $610 million requested by the Navy for DD-963s in the fiscal 1973 budget was reduced to $247million, and additional cuts could be mandated if Litton and the Navy don't shape up in the near future.

The 'Spruance's' will be 6,900 tons fully loaded, 560 feet long, 54 feet at the beam, and capable of somewhat over 30 knots. Principal mission will be ASW, but they will also have 'significant' shore bombardment and AA capabilities. LAMPS helicopters, SEA SPARROW missiles, ASROC (anti-submarine rocket), and 5in guns will be the principal armament.

**POLARIS-to-POSEIDON:** Some 31 of the 41-ship POLARIS FBM (Fleet Ballistic Missile) force will eventually convert to the longer range POSEIDON. The 'Lafayette'-class ships are 425 feet long, 33 feet at the beam, displace 8,250 tons submerged, and carry 16 missiles which in the POSEIDON configuration will be MIRVed – ie, designed to carry up to 14 (depending on range) Multiple Independently-targetable Re-entry Vehicles or warheads.

The POLARIS A-2 has a range of about 1,500 nautical miles, the A-3 (carried by the latter 23 of the 31-ship 'Lafayette' class) a range of about 2,500 nautical miles, and the POSEIDON a range of about 3,000 nautical miles. (Note: In Navy public relations parlance, 'about' indicates a maximum potential often considerably greater than the performance characteristics released to the press. Thus, the official top submerged speed of a POLARIS/POSEIDON submarine is 'about' 30 knots or so, but knowledgeable sources indicate the real top speed is considerably higher.)

The extended range and MIRV capabilities of the POSEIDON have convinced Congress the programme is worthwhile, so there should be no funding problems. But there may be political problems – the anti-military bloc in Congress for some reason believes improvement of the FBM missile system equates to an increase in the system's longevity. Navy

The United States Navy's destroyer force is now rapidly becoming obsolete. The new 'Spruance' class destroyers are urgently needed to replace these old destroyers. Unfortunately the contractors, Litton Industries, now expect delays to the programme, mainly as a result of delays to the LHA, for which they also are the prime contractors./*Official USN*

At the moment the American Navy and Congress are undecided whether to concentrate on the new Trident Programme or on the 'Los Angeles' class of nuclear attack submarines (shown here in the artist's sketch). At the moment funds have been provided for both programmes./*Official USN*

officials have been diligent in their efforts to convince Congress that such is not the case. Because of the particularly heavy structural stresses imposed on the FBM submarines, they say, a 20-year life expectancy for the POLARIS/POSEIDON boats (which operate at 'about '400 feet, or considerably deeper) may be all that can be reasonably expected. The POLARIS 'Lafayette' class were all commissioned between April 23rd 1963 and April 1st 1967, which means, from a Navy viewpoint, at least, that the new TRIDENT fleet will have to be on station and aready no later than 1985 or so.

**Nuclear Attack Submarines:** The Navy, and Congress, have been a bit schizoid about priorities, debating whether it is better to go ahead with full funding on the underseas deterrent (POLARIS/POSEIDON/TRIDENT) first, or to give top priority to the nuclear attack submarine to protect American cities from the Soviet FBM threat. Happily, from a submariner's point of view, Congress has, so far, decided to fund both programmes generously – sometimes at the expense of other pro-

grammes which the Navy or other Services consider of even higher priority.

The SSN-688 ('Los Angeles'-class) nuclear attack submarine programme represents a classic clash between the Executive and Legislative branches of the United States Government. Congress has voted more money for the programme than the Defence Department requested. Navy witnesses have made it clear, moreover, that the Navy is quite willing to proceed at flank speed, providing funds are available, but that Defence Department and White House officials want to stretch out the programme somewhat to make funds available for other systems. "Included in this year's budget is a request for long lead time funding for (deleted) SSNs to be procured next year," Navy spokesmen told the Senate Armed Services Committee during hearings on the fiscal 1973 budget. "A return to the level of (deleted) SSNs per year does not indicate a desire to reduce our procurement, but rather is dictated by fiscal constraints imposed by the requirements of other new programmes and the general effect of the rising cost of military procurement."

The SSN-688 programme is, however, something special. The 17 ships already fully- or partially-funded (of an estimated 25–30 ships planned) represent a quantum advance in anti-submarine capabilities which, with various highly classified underwater sonar surveillance systems and other programmes now on the drawing board should be able to blunt, if not destroy, the Soviet undersea deterrent force. The SSN-688 is 6,900 tons submerged, 360 feet long, 33 feet at the beam, capable of 30+ knot speed and well equipped for ASW with the SUBROC nuclear depth bomb missile and new – capable, but 'controversial' (because of cost overruns) – Mark 48 acoustic homing torpedoes.

In addition to the 'high speed' 688s the Navy is building a 'quiet design' submarine – USS *Glenard P. Lipscomb*, due to be commissioned in mid- or late-1974 – and a new class of boats carrying tactical cruise missiles. The latter, planned for use against enemy surface combatants, is still only in the planning stage.

**Nuclear Guided Missile Frigate:** " . . For the nuclear frigate programme, the future remains bleak". So spoke doughty Vice Admiral Hyman G. Rickover, fulltime father of the United States Navy's nuclear ship programme, and parttime national gadfly, in fiscal 1973 testimony before the House Defence Appropriations Subcommittee. He was referring to a 1971 Defence Department decision not to build two nuclear frigates previously authorised by Congress. The seven nuclear frigates already operational or under construction will, with the nuclear-powered guided missile cruiser *Long Beach*, form escorts for two nuclear carriers – which means, in other words, there will be two other nuclear carriers with *no* escorts.

The Navy originally planned building no fewer than 28 DLGNs, but the high cost ($250million per ship, by some estimates) caused an agonizing budgetary reappraisal. An all-nuclear task force would, as Rickover diligently points out in his annual appearances on Capitol Hill, represent a naval armada without equal, possessing awesome power, incredible speed, and virtually unlimited range. But it would cost a billion for the carrier, another billion for the escorts, and another billion or more for the aircraft. Whether the programme will be revived or not is debatable. At the time of writing, however, it seems unlikely.

The Navy does get a good ship for its money. The three latest (DLGN-38-class)

nuclear frigates will enter the fleet in the 1975–77 period. Each will displace 10,000 tons fully loaded, be 585 feet long, 61 feet at the beam, and capable of 30+ knots. Two ASW helicopters, two combination twin TARTAR-D/ASROC launchers, two 5in/54 guns, and torpedoes will constitute the principal armament. In addition to its escort role the DLGN could be used in surveillance/shadowing, barrier patrol, and limited sea control missions.

**Escort Ships:** The 46 ships of the 'Knox'-class, largest post-World War II American class built from the same design, typify the problems plaguing today's Navy. Construction delays and mounting costs led at least one distinguished critic to call the DE-1052s "the greatest mistake in ship procurement that the Navy has known".

Cost and construction delay criticism is justifiable, but complaints have also been voiced about the ship's lack of versatility, its relatively slow speed (27 knots), and its 'vulnerability' – one turbine and one shaft, with no back-up engineering capability. Answering such criticisms in order, Navy spokesmen point out that the 1052s were planned and authorised as 'single purpose' ocean escorts. Their speed, say programme managers, is more than sufficient for that job (and is really somewhat higher than the 27 knots officially admitted), and the redundancy provided by a second engineering plant would not be worth the extra cost. Besides, the ship has, in fact, 'performed well' with fast carriers, a task for which it was 'not designed'.

Whether the critics or defenders are right is now irrelevant. The 1052s will be the Navy's principal ocean escort for a long time to come. And it should be well suited to its single purpose mission. The 4,100-ton ship is 438 feet long and 48 feet at the beam. Principal armament includes the LAMPS helicopter, Mk 32 torpedoes, ASROC, SEA SPARROW BPDMS missile system, and one 5in/54 dual purpose gun. Some ships will also carry the STANDARD interim Surface-to-surface missile.

**AAW Destroyer/Destroyer Leader:** Some 19 guided missile destroyer leaders (DLGs) have been, or are being, proposed for funding in the fiscal 1966–74 budgets. Modernisation provides them the capability to launch either the Homing TERRIER or the STANDARD missile from the same launcher – they are also being equipped with the Navy Tactical Data System, an improved three-dimensional air search radar, and an improved guided missile fire control system. The combined effect, Navy spokesmen told Congress, will be "increased target acquisition, range and a markedly reduced reaction time with a greater kill probability."

Funding will also be requested within the next few years, according to present Navy plans, for a relatively large class of new guided missile destroyers and destroyer leaders to replace current 'carrier capable' DDGs and DLGs reaching retirement age in the early- and mid-1980s. Principal mission of the new class (or classes) will be anti-air warfare, but they will also have considerable ASW capabilities as well. STANDARD medium and extended range missiles will probably be carried. The HARPOON anti-ship missile and LAMPS helicopter are also likely possibilities.

The new ships named, plus those already in the fleet, are, of course, important principally because of the weapons and aircraft they carry. Therefore, ignoring the POLARIS/POSEIDON/TRIDENT missile programmes previously discussed, other missiles and aircraft already operational, and various gun systems (still of some, but diminishing, importance), a brief look at 'current procurement' aircraft and missiles might nevertheless be instructive.

Principal Air-to-air missiles in the current buy category include SPARROW, SIDEWINDER, and PHOENIX. The 'semi-active' radar-guided SPARROW is designed to provide American aircraft all-aspect all-weather capability against high performance enemy aircraft. The less capable SIDEWINDER is a short-range infrared homing missile. The PHOENIX, planned for use with the F-14 fighter, is supersonic, all-weather, long range, and equipped with anti-jam devices.

SHRIKE and CONDOR are the only Air-to-ground missiles now being procured for the Navy, but HARPOON can be launched from either ships or aircraft. SHRIKE is an anti-radar missile; CONDOR, just now moving out

of the RDT&E category into procurement, is an electro-optical guided, medium-range, supersonic cruise missile designed for use against 'selected high priority land and sea targets in heavily defended areas'; and HARPOON (also still mostly in the RDT&E stage, but with initial procurement beginning in fiscal 1974) is an anti-ship missile.

The STANDARD missile family includes the supersonic medium-range Surface-to-air STANDARD, which provides all-weather anti-air and Surface-to-surface armament for destroyer types; the extended range STANDARD, which provides the same for cruisers, aircraft carriers, and guided missile frigates; the SSM (Surface-to-surface) STANDARD (still in RDT&E), which provides an anti-radiation defensive capability for surface ships; and the STANDARD ARM (anti-radiation missile) Air-to-surface anti-radar missile (procured in fiscal 1973, but not in the fiscal 1974 budget).

Naval combat aircraft in the current procurement category include:

(a) The A-6E Intruder, a two-seat, twin-engine, all-weather, long-range jet attack aircraft which can deliver nuclear or conventional ordnance against moving land or sea targets.
(b) The EA-6B Prowler, a four-seat, twin-engine derivative of the A-6 used for tactical jamming of enemy radars or communications.
(c) The A-7E Corsair II, a single-seat, single-engine, jet attack aircraft with subsonic, medium-range, visual attack capability 'of extreme accuracy and high payload' and used in tactical support and interdiction missions.
(d) The AV-8A Harrier, a single-seat, single-jet, transonic light attack V/STOL, already operational with the Marine Corps, but planned for possible use on carriers and/or Sea Control Ships.
(e) The F-4J Phantom, a two-seat, twin-engine, turbo-jet, all-weather fighter equipped with Air-to-air missiles for its primary fleet air defence role, and with a variety of bombs and rockets for its secondary role as an attack aircraft.
(f) The F-14A Tomcat, a two-seat, variable-sweep-wing, twin-engine, supersonic jet all-weather fleet air defence fighter with Air-to-

air and Air-to-surface attack capabilities. (Rather large cost overruns have earned the Tomcat a 'controversial' label, but most experts agree it is an exceedingly capable aircraft, no matter what the price tag.)

(g) The P-3C Orion, a four-engine, land-based, high-speed, turbo-prop, ASW patrol aircraft, also capable of aerial mining and destruction of coastal shipping.

(h) The S-3A Viking, a subsonic, twin-engine, sea-based, all-weather, long-range ASW aircraft planned for use on the CV multi-mission carrier.

(i) The E-2C Hawkeye, a five-seat, twin-engine, turbo-prop, carrier-based, early-warning aircraft, also used for control of strike aircraft.

Included in the 'other aircraft' category are the T-2C Buckeye and TAV-8A Harrier trainers, and the EC-130Q Hercules, which provides the Navy an airborne communications relay interfacing with other United States national Command and Control authorities.

Helicopters in the current buy category include the UH-1N Iroquois, or Huey, used for troop transport, medical evacuation, and other 'utility' chores, and the CH-53 Sea Stallion lift helicopter (in the RDT&E stage) designed to handle loads up to 16 tons. Also in the RDT&E budget is the Army-Navy HLH (Heavy Lift Helicopter), designed to carry $22\frac{1}{2}$ tons. The SH-2D Sealite (a converted UH-2 Seasprite) is planned for use in the ASW LAMPS helicopter role, but is not likely to be funded in the fiscal 1974 budget.

Other hardware programmes worth noting are the CIWS (Close-In Weapon System), a unitized gun weapon system of 20mm size designed to provide rapid-reaction light-weight defence against anti-ship missiles and low flying aircraft, the Mk 48 torpedo previously mentioned, and the CAPTOR (encapsulated torpedo) anti-submarine mine.

Finally, returning to current well-publicised personnel problems, it is obvious the Navy will need highly qualified and well trained technicians to man the extremely complex weapons systems now in the fleet, on the ways, or on the drawing boards. The search is for quality.

But, unlike the Marine Corps with its 'few good men' slogan, the Navy needs 'quite a few' good men.

The end of the draft has created numerous problems for all United States services, but especially for the Navy, which suffers from long deployments and heavy operational schedules almost as much in peacetime as in war.

To combat the accumulated barnacles of many years of personnel neglect Admiral Zumwalt issued his famous string of 'Z-Grams' shortly after taking office. Many of the reforms he instituted were undoubtedly long overdue. Others, many think, swung the pendulum too far in the other direction and created an air of permissiveness – this, at least, was the opinion many persons of influence held after the racial incidents aboard various ships in late 1972. What was not emphasized was that most of the black sailors involved are in what educators call the 'low achiever' category, accepted into the Navy under a social programme 'quota' system imposed by higher echelon officials, but with little hope of advancement. The accumulated frustrations of long deployments, killing work schedules, and dead-end job situations ended, naturally, in some rather violent explosions. Such problems, unfortunately, are likely to continue.

Similar problems could develop with the assignment of women to combat ships, – which may be inevitable when the so-called equal rights amendment is ratified by the states. The problem here – as most women instinctively know – is not the physical intimacy which may occasionally result, but the long-enduring emotional and personal bonds which could develop when attractive young men and young women are thrown into daily working and living situations. The modern Navy is basically a married Navy, but no Navy wife will be willing to live with that situation any longer than she can help it. What the answers are to the US Navy's current racial unrest and its probable future sexual turmoil no one knows. But there's probably no other Navy in the world, and no other nation in the world, which would so blithely (not to say blindly) create such problems for itself.

# The Soviet Underwater Threat

ANTHONY J. WATTS

The greatest threat the free nations of the world face today is that posed by the Russian submarine. To understand present Russian submarine philosophy and to assess its strength and capabilities it is necessary to look at the past history of this force.

Contrary to public belief in the West the Russian Navy has not in the past been quite the impotent weapon that many would have us believe. For instance during World War I the Russians were the first to develop the idea of a well-balanced, self-contained strike force, operating a formation of seaplane carriers accompanied by battleships and screened by cruisers and destroyers. They were also the first navy to develop amphibious warfare techniques, employing specially designed flat-bottomed landing craft and an artificial harbour. The Russians, then, have not been slow to develop new techniques of naval warfare, nor to introduce new types of warship, even if sometimes these have been of foreign design.

Such a new type of vessel first introduced into the Russian Navy in 1880, but designed by a foreign power, was the submarine. However, as in many other navies at that time this revolutionary warship was looked upon with great scepticism by the Russian Naval High Command. Gradually, however, the Russian Naval Staff, with little enthusiasm, came to accept the concept of the submarine. They ignored the offensive potential of the craft and put their faith in its ability for use as a defensive weapon, a strategy which the Russians held to be proper for the submarine right up to the end of World War II.

The disastrous war with Japan, which culminated in the defeat of the Russian Navy at Tsushima, left the navy decimated. The economy of the country was in a parlous state, and there was little money available for military purposes. Future naval strategy thus placed the emphasis on *defence* rather than *offence*. In the programme designed to re-build the navy submarines were placed well down on the list of priorities, only six being ordered in the 1908 Programme (three for the Baltic and three for the Black Sea). The following year a new Ten Year Programme of construction, designed to give the navy a total of 38 submarines (Baltic 20, Black Sea 6, Pacific 12) by 1920, was put forward. The Government, however, was unwilling to spend the large sum of money that would be required to complete the whole programme, and not until 1911 did the Duma authorise the implementation of the programme. Known as 'The Great Ship-building Programme' submarine construction was to be spread over a longer period (36 submarines to be completed for the Baltic Fleet by 1930, not 1920) and emphasis was placed on the Baltic theatre of operations, the Black Sea being regarded as a minor area, the Fleet there having limitations placed on its movements by the Dardanelles, and whoever controlled them. In spite of the fact that the new programme had been passed, funds were still not forthcoming from the treasury, and in the end only half the number of submarines were ordered.

One of the submarines ordered was of a completely new type designed for mine warfare, a field in which the Russians excelled, and were generally acknowledged as the world's experts. Although the *Krab*, as the new minelaying submarine was called, was the first to be designed in the world, she was not the first to be completed. Substandard workmanship and the chaotic state of Russian industry as a whole, which just could not cope with the demands made upon it, resulted in the *Krab* taking seven years to complete. By this time both the British and German Navy's were operating minelaying submarines. Not only was there a deplorable delay in completing the *Krab*, but when she finally entered service there were found to be so many faults that she was dubbed a failure. The faults were not solely attributable to the

Above: The first class of submarine to be constructed by the Russians after World War II was the 'W' class. It is estimated that about 145 of these craft are still in service. Here a 'W' class submarine refuels a helicopter somewhere in the Pacific./Novosti

Below: Parallel with the construction of the 'W' class ran the 25 vessels of the 'Z' class. They incorporated a number of design features of the German war built Type XXI submarine./MoD, RN, Official

poor workmanship; in a number of cases the actual design was found to be lacking in certain essentials. So although the Russians were not short of ideas, their industry and technology was just not up to the standard needed to produce such sophisticated weapons systems. (They had, after all, only just emerged from an industrial revolution, an event which had occurred in Europe and Britain almost a century before).

With the political situation in Europe rapidly deteriorating, the 1914 Programme provided for a total of 18 submarines to be constructed as quickly as possible (12 for the Baltic and six for the Black Sea). With Russian industry in such a backward state it had been policy for some time past to order much of the technical equipment needed from Germany, in particular the diesel motors. With the outbreak of war in 1914 all this flow of material ceased, and serious delays occurred in the completion of the submarines. (Of the 28 submarines available at the outbreak of war, only four were operational). Such were the depths of improvisation that the Russians were forced to take in order to get submarines operational, that they dismantled the low powered engines from a number of river monitors and installed them in the submarines. The delays and setbacks which arose meant that many of the submarines did not enter service until 1917. When the Revolution broke out in November 1917, putting an end to Russia's military efforts in World War I, there were about 70 submarines still on the stocks.

Russian submarine operations were at a very low level during World War I. This was due to a number of reasons, not the least of these being the obsolete nature of those submarines in service, and the serious delays occurring in the completion of new vessels. Other factors also contributed to the inactivity of the Russian submarines. For these one has to look back to pre-war naval strategy, which placed the emphasis on defence, rather than offence. Very few provisions had been made for any sort of submarine campaign, and very little effort had been put into making the submarines, or their crews, ready for war. With the higher echelons of the Russian Navy

failing to appreciate the potentialities of the submarine it was hardly surprising that training, on the whole, was of rather a low standard, and submarine commanders had little appreciation of their role in the war, and were not encouraged to use their initiative and develop submarine tactics when on patrol; add to this the obsolete vessels and the poor nature of the equipment, and one is surprised that any significant results were obtained at all.

The Baltic formed the main area of operations during World War I, where the Fleet was to support land operations by the Army, carrying out bombardments and landings. A major policy of offensive mine warfare was developed with the laying of large minefields in strategic positions, thus denying free passage to German shipping in the confined areas of the Baltic, coupled with large defensive minefields laid off the major ports.

As a result of the low level of submarine activity development of the weapon failed to receive the impetus from war conditions that one normally associates with warship evolution in wartime. Again the backward state of Russian industry and the lack of organisation and chaotic conditions prevailing behind the front had a serious effect. The result was that few new designs for submarines were drawn up and little technological progress made with their equipment. Poor operational results can also, to some extent, explain the lack of progress in this field of naval warfare. For instance 14 submarine patrols were undertaken in the Baltic in 1914, but in spite of the profusion of targets, both merchant and warship, the Russian submarines failed to score any success. Towards the end of 1915 submarine patrols became more intensive, but again inadequate training and obsolete equipment led to poor results. Of 50 torpedoes fired in the Baltic during 1915, not one hit its target. By 1916 a total of 27 submarines were in service in the Baltic, but in spite of the greater frequency of patrols only five vessels were sunk. Lack of spares and inadequate repair facilities soon began to make themselves felt; overhauls and refits took longer and longer, so that by November 1917 only one submarine remained operational.

With the end of the civil war the Soviets put in hand a new programme of construction designed to rebuild the navy. By 1933 they had managed to get a total of 33 submarines into service (Black Sea 18, Baltic 6, White Sea 1, Volga River/Caspian Sea area 8). This disposition at once shows a surprising shift in emphasis concerning which areas were regarded as being most important. Regarding submarine operations the Baltic as a major area had fallen into disfavour. There were a number of reasons for this, the main one being the fact that many of the bases were closed by ice during the winter months. The Black Sea had numerous bases which were not subject to the same limitations posed by weather conditions, and more important, they had suffered less damage from the ravages of the Revolution. The other interesting feature is the stationing of eight submarines in the area of the Caspian Sea. This was the first time that submarines had been reported in this area, although small naval forces had been based there before. The Caspian Sea provided an excellent area for the training of submarine crews, and was to remain so right up to the present.

By 1926 the Russians had once again managed to enlist technical assistance from the Germans. Following Russo/German arms talks a naval mission from Germany, headed by the official U-boat historian of World War I – Admiral Spindler, spent some time in Russia discussing the various requirements of the Soviets in connection with the reconstruction of their navy. The Germans were asked for plans of their most successful type of submarine (Type B-III which was later developed into the successful VIIC Type used during World War II), the service of certain technical experts, and most significant of all, details of U-boat operational experience gained during the war. With all these details to hand the Russians would be in an excellent position to catch up, and possibly overtake, any other power then operating submarines.

Feeling the need to rapidly give their new navy some teeth, and bearing in mind the defensively, as opposed to offensively, orientated strategy, the Russians realised that the submarine was a weapon ideally suited to their needs. Compared to a large and costly surface fleet, submarines were relatively cheap and simple to build, they could be constructed quickly in large numbers, and there would be great savings in manpower (a real problem since the war and Revolution when the navy lost nearly all its officers and large numbers of men). In 1928 the Russians embarked on a new Ten Year Programme of construction, with the main emphasis placed on the construction of submarines, which would now form the new *Force-de-Resistance*. By 1931 the Russians officially stated that they had 16 submarines in commission, the first of which – the 'D' class based on an Italian design – had entered service in 1929. These were followed by the 'L' class, based on the captured British *L55*. In 1930 the Chief Commissar set out the future policy of the Russian Navy which in effect was no different from that of World War I, namely that the Navy was to act in support of the Army, providing afloat support for land operations. The Navy was to refrain from seeking any major engagement with an enemy, but was to contain its activities near the coastline where defensive minefields, submarines and naval aircraft could play a major role. With its future role firmly laid down the Navy set about implementing it with a renewed programme of construction. With operations tied to a coastal role there was no longer any need for large ocean going submarines, and so submarine construction over the next few years concentrated on smaller craft able to implement the naval policy. The 'M' class coastal craft were designed in 1933 and were pre-fabricated inland and shipped to sea ports where they were assembled. Plans were put in hand for the mass production of this class, but the outbreak of World War II with the resulting shortage of materials, coupled with the breakdown of much of the industrial effort when many factories and production plants were dismantled and shipped to the east to escape from the Germans, meant that these plans were never fulfilled.

By 1936 Official German sources credited the Russian Fleet with a total of 116 submarines, and stated that by 1937 the Russians would have the largest submarine fleet in the world with a total of about 150 boats. The backbone of the Russian submarine fleet was formed with the 'Shch' class medium size ocean-going boats. As a result of naval policy which concentrated naval efforts near the coast, these boats were given only a limited radius of action. It was at this point that Stalin began his great purge. In the space of two years (1937–38) the majority of senior naval officers were either executed or sent to labour camps. As a result junior officers and NCO's who escaped the excesses of the purge were rapidly promoted to posts they were often incapable of holding, while in turn their places in the fleet were taken by raw seamen who had only just left the training schools.

These purges left a deplorable gap in the Soviet Navy which was to have dire consequencies on its efforts during World War II.

When Russia was dragged into the war in June 1941 the Fleet had a total of 276 submarines in commission with a futther 51 under construction. These were distributed as follows:

Baltic 76 (+ 34 building), Arctic 45, Black Sea 68 (+ 10 building), and Pacific 87 (+ 7 building).

With the outbreak of war work on submarines under construction slowed right down, although a number were completed during the war, but at such a slow rate that they barely kept pace with the losses.

The main area of submarine operations during the war was the Arctic, in contrast to the Baltic during World War I. This was due to a number of reasons. In the Baltic the Russians were forced on the defensive and retreated right back to Leningrad which was besieged: coupled with the vast minefields laid by the Germans, submarine operations in the Baltic were thus severely restricted. From such operations as the submarines in this area were able to conduct during four years of war only 51 ships were sunk for the loss of an equal number of Soviet submarines. Results in the Black Sea were even worse, where for a loss of 34 submarines only 32 vessels were sunk, but this included losses incurred while submarines were engaged in

supply missions to beleaguered fortresses. Here, as in the Baltic, the Soviets had been forced to abandon most of their major ports and were left with only a few minor bases which were ill equipped for the support of naval operations. Axis minefields had a further restrictive effect on submarine operations in the Black Sea.

The Pacific Fleet only became involved in the war for the last seven days, just before the Japanese surrendered. The Russians had not declared war on the Japanese previously as they were too heavily committed to the conduct of the war in the West. The Arctic thus formed the main area of submarine operations for the Russians during World War II. Here the Russians had available two ports, which although subject to German air attack (they were never really threatened with attack from the land) nevertheless formed suitable bases for operations. Their geographical position was well suited to Arctic operations and general conditions in the area were ideal for submarine operations. In spite of these favourable factors Russian submarines were still unable to show very good results. Submarine losses in the Arctic amounted to a total of 25, for which the Russians could claim a total of 45 enemy vessels sunk.

The poor results of submarine operations during the war can be attributed directly to the effects of Stalin's terrible pre-war purges and the effects of the Revolution in 1917. This led to a totally unimaginative control being exercised over the submarine branch for fear of falling foul of the regime. This was combined with a poor tactical and strategical concept of submarine warfare. The absolute control exercised by the submarine high command did not permit individual submarine commanders to exercise any initiative whatsoever, and to ensure that they did not deviate from their orders, or attempt any moves which might not fit in with ideological concepts, each boat carried a political commissar who was given overall responsibility for the crew of the submarine. In order to placate the submarine officers this 'civil servant' – come political watchdog was given an acting naval rank. In addition the pre-war purges had severely curtailed training schemes with the result that seamanship was generally of rather poor quality and fell far short of the requirements for the waging of successful naval operations. There was however, no lack of courage among individuals, even to the extent in some cases of what might be called foolhardiness, or perhaps these actions were a result of the political necessity of adhering rigidly to orders! Losses in ships and men were not regarded as of any consequence if results could be achieved, which, unfortunately, they often weren't.

The end of World War II in 1945 failed to solve, as far as the Russians were concerned, any of the maritime problems which faced them. On land victories had secured for the Soviet Union a vast area of satellite countries which would provide a strong buffer to absorb and dissipate any land attack from the West. At sea, however, the same problems were inherent as before the war, but of a much deadlier nature. Basically the trouble lay with Russia's vast and vulnerable coastline, which if left unprotected would offer perfect vantage points from which a seaborne assault could be launched to outflank any Russian moves on land, and from where carrier forces could launch air attacks on the industrial centres.

Defence of the coastline in 1945 was to Stalin of the utmost importance, especially in view of the devastating possibilities of nuclear attack, which it was not difficult to foresee could at some time in the not too distant future be launched from carriers. In 1946, therefore, Stalin announced a new 20-year programme of construction aimed at building up Russian Naval forces and in fact carrying on where they had been forced to leave off in 1941 when Germany had invaded the Soviet Union.

The war had shown up numerous faults in the Russian Navy, such as insufficient training, technical faults and many deficiencies of various sorts. The first and most important task was to rebuild and repair the shipyards which had suffered such severe damage during the war. Much use was made of material captured in East Germany and by 1948, with the assistance of captured German technicians, the Soviets had largely managed to put back into operation the majority of their shipyards. With so many yards having to be almost completely rebuilt it was possible for the Russians to redesign the yards and put them on a modern footing, capable of building vessels using the latest construction and mass production techniques. Having rebuilt the shipyards it was then possible to commence work on the reconstruction of the Fleet. There were two main, and rather conflicting requirements. Firstly it was necessary to build up the strength of the Fleet as quickly as possible to meet the threat from the West; and secondly to incorporate the technological advances made by the Allies and Germans during the war. In order to meet these commitments the Russians instituted a crash programme of construction to be completed in six years. To meet this deadline they were forced to use obsolete designs equipping the vessels with such improved armaments and equipment as was to hand. Once again the submarine formed the major part of this programme with a total of 145 'W' class submarines of a 1944 design. Completed between 1949 and 1956 the 'W' class formed the backbone of the new Soviet fleet, whose basis was quantity rather than quality.

At this time Soviet naval strategy was still to a large extent based on pre-war ideas, which were updated to meet the new threat from the West. Thus defence of the homeland, as far as the Navy was concerned, entailed an outlying force of submarines deployed in dense formations. Their task was to engage any enemy carrier forces preparing to launch what might well turn out to be a nuclear attack. Because of the fairly limited radius of action of carrier aircraft at that time such an action was deemed to occur in reasonably close proximity to the Russian coastline. Behind this forward line of submarines would be defensive minefields patrolled by squadrons of heavily armed surface warships ready to attack such of the enemy as escaped the submarine patrol lines and minefields. It was envisaged that the complete action would occur under the protective umbrella of aircraft of the Soviet Navy.

Such a strategy as this obviously demanded

*Above:* A 'ZV' class submarine. These vessels were converted to carry the first Russian ICBM—the SARK. Two missiles are carried in vertical tubes in the conning tower./*Official USN*

*Right:* 'W' class Long-Bin conversion. Note the enormous structure that the conning tower has become./*A. J. Watts collection*

*Below right:* 'F' class attack submarine. This is the largest class of Russian submarines built since the war. They are an improved design of the 'Z' class./*Official USN*

large numbers of submarines, for there were four fleets covering the Soviet coastline – the Northern, Baltic, Black Sea and Pacific Fleets, in addition to a number of small river flotillas – and in each of these fleets the Soviets could never expect to have more than 50 per cent of their effective submarine fleet available for action at any one time. To meet these needs it was estimated that each fleet would require between 250 and 300 submarines, and this was born out in 1948 when it was hinted that a total of 1,200 submarines would be constructed during the 1950s. There were many in the West who viewed this proposition with considerable alarm, for they felt, falsely as it so happens at the time, that this fleet was being prepared for a campaign against the merchant fleets of the West, similar to the German submarine campaigns of World War I and II, which had so nearly defeated the Allies. A submarine campaign against merchant shipping, however, was not the purpose of this fleet, instead the Soviets planned to use their underwater fleet in a similar fashion to the Japanese submarine fleet of World War II, ie as part of the main battle fleet to be used in action against enemy warships. Fortunately for the West Russian strategy at that time was at fault. The Japanese submarine campaign had ended in disaster for their fleet, and in their study of submarine warfare the Russians either failed to take note of, or did not wish to take note of, a number of other very important points concerning these submarine campaigns. Thus it was that the Russians preferred to accept Japanese claims of American warships sunk by their submarines rather than American denials of these claims, partly because of an enormous anti-American campaign at that time, and partly because the facts so presented fitted in with what the Soviets wished to believe submarines could achieve and because it would fit the purpose they had in mind for their huge submarine fleet. In addition the Russians were only aware of the failure of two German submarine campaigns; they failed completely to realise how close to defeat the Allies were at certain times during these campaigns. So very few Russian merchantmen sailed in Atlantic or Arctic convoys that few

of their people saw or heard of the disastrous losses suffered by the Allies, and the Russians looked upon our figures of merchant ships lost as highly exaggerated. Not only this but further convincing proof was the fact that Russian submarines had managed to sink so few enemy merchant ships themselves, in spite of 'heroic' attacks by their commanders.

Between 1946 and 1949 the master spy Klaus Fuchs passed the secrets of the Atomic Bomb to the Russians. Apart from being in a position to develop their own atomic weapons and catch up on the West, the Russians were then also in a position to harness the enormous energy developed during the process of fission for use in propulsion systems. The tremendous advantages to be gained from such a propulsion system were not lost upon the Russians and the decision to build a submarine propelled by nuclear power was taken about 1949. It was expected that the first unit using a nuclear propulsion unit would be in service by about 1958. With the details of the atomic bomb the Russians began developing nuclear warheads of their own, and by 1953 they had managed to engineer such a warhead for use on a torpedo, which was soon in production.

In the meantime the Soviet navy had under construction, almost parallel with the 'W' class, 25 vessels of the 'Z' class. These vessels were a mixture of ideas, some being based on the design of the German war built Type XXI (a number of which the Russians had captured, together with their design engineers and constructors), while certain constructional features were based on the Russian's own pre-war designed 'K' class. Here again, however, Russian technology and industry failed to keep pace with naval requirements. On some of the early vessels of the 'Z' class the Russians had attempted to couple a development of the German war designed Walter turbine to the centre shaft, but difficulties were experienced, and entry of the early boats into front line service was delayed for over a year while engineers tried to iron out the problems, without success, for the vessels finally joined the fleet with an ordinary diesel motor coupled to the centre shaft.

The problems encountered with the 'Z'

class are typical of what happened with the development procedure adopted in the Russian services. Basically when developing any new piece of equipment it is standard Russian practice to rush the first model into service as quickly as possible, where it can be evaluated. While this is being done, on any vessel available virtually, a new vessel is designed to carry the initial model of the item. Then having ironed out any problems arising, and there are often many, as will be seen later in this article, a completely new vessel is designed to mount the weapon, engine or whatever, in its final form, incorporating any modifications deemed necessary during its evaluation. The Russians hope that by adopting such a system they will be able to make up some of the leeway they have lost on advances made by the West. The true outcome, of course, is that because of the resulting problems, breakdowns and delays associated with introducing a system into service before it has been finally proved, that system has often not reached its ultimate possible development, and is often obsolescent when it reaches full front line service.

With the construction of the 'W' and 'Z' classes the Russians also introduced a new standard 21in torpedo based on the German model and fitted with such refinements as a homing device, pattern running machinery and possibly electric drive, although with what success these innovations were introduced it is impossible to say, suffice it to mention that, as stated above, a torpedo with a nuclear warhead was available in 1953, and so this weapon must be regarded as highly successful for the Russians to have deemed it practicable to have developed such a warhead for them.

In 1953, the year Stalin died, the Russians tested their first H-bomb. It was decided at this time that if the Russian Navy was to be at all effective in the nuclear age then greater emphasis must be placed upon technology and the gearing of Russian industry to cope with rapid technological advances. This in turn would place greater strain on the scientists and engineers who would have to keep abreast of these advances, especially those in the West, and in particular those of America

and Great Britain, if the Russian Navy were to present any effective form of defence against those navies and NATO. Thus while the scientists at home were hard at work designing and developing new machinery, weapons and equipment, agents abroad were collecting as much information as they could lay hands on concerning the advances being made in foreign navies.

In accordance with this policy of keeping abreast of advances in the West, and in an effort to present some form of antidote to the POLARIS programme then under development in America, the Russians began, during the middle 1950s to experiment with the possibilities of submarines carrying short range missiles. With these it would be possible to pose a threat at least to the coastal cities of the United States. The first experiments were based on a development of the German Laffarentz Project, the plans and details of which the Russians had captured at Peenemünde. The basic plan was for a Type XXI submarine to tow a V-2 rocket in a submersible container. When the launch position was reached the container would be brought to the vertical position by trimming with compressed air so that the rocket's nose just broke the surface of the water. The rocket was then fuelled manually from tanks in the container and fired electrically by cable from the submarine. Three such rockets could be towed by each submarine. The disadvantages of such a system are obvious. Firstly, as there were manual operations to be carried out, it was necessary to surface the submarine in what might well turn out to be enemy dominated waters. There was always the possibility that the tow might part, and even if it did not, the manoeuvrability of the submarine was severely restricted under such conditions. Last, but by no means least, there was the inherent danger in handling the highly volatile liquid fuel. The Russians were able to overcome a number of these problems, but in so doing created others that were not so easily solved. Serious problems were encountered with the guidance of the rockets and also with the launchers and the project was finally abandoned in favour of the SHADDOCK rocket.

Above: 'G' class submarines. The left-hand picture shows a G-I type submarine. The first vessels of this class were delayed during construction due to problems with the missile system. The G-I class are fitted with two launching tubes for the SARK missile. The later G-II type shown in the right-hand picture was fitted with three launching tubes for the SERB missile./*Official USN*

Below: 'W' class canvas-bag conversion. Note the large tracking radar aerial used for mid-course guidance with the early versions of the SHADDOCK missile./*Official USN*

Foot: Nuclear-powered 'E-II' class submarine. Note the indentations where the launchers for the eight SHADDOCK missiles are sited./*Official USN*

About the same time as these experiments were in progress other development work commenced on the design of a long range rocket capable of carrying a nuclear warhead – the Inter-Continental Ballistic Missile (ICBM). Parallel with this development the Russians began drawing up plans for two classes of submarine capable of carrying the missile. This was a typical example of the Russian system of development procedure. The two classes in question were the 'G' and 'H'. The 'G' was a conventionally powered submarine that was already in the design stage as an attack submarine. The design was so altered to enable the boats of this class to carry the first ICBMs in the conning tower. At the same time a completely new design – the 'H' – was drawn up specifically to operate ICBM missiles. In addition this design was to be nuclear powered and based on the system then under development for the 'N' class and which at that time had not even been proved in service, or even fully tested.

In 1954 a new type of attack submarine was introduced into the Soviet Navy. The Russians had at long last managed to perfect the Walter system sufficiently to design a new class – the 'Q' – around it. Even so they still encountered problems with the turbine, so much so that, combined with the knowledge that a nuclear propulsion unit would be available in the not too distant future, only 15 boats of this class were built instead of the 96 planned, and these entered service three years later than planned. Finally the Russian developed Walter turbine proved so unreliable that the shaft was coupled to a conventional diesel/electric motor.

By 1956 development of the Russian ICBM had reached the stage where it could be fitted in a warship. The 'G' and 'H' class were already in the design stage but construction was as yet not sufficiently advanced to enable them to test the missile. Accordingly a number of 'Z' class submarines were taken in hand while still under construction and the conning tower altered and lengthened so that the vessels could carry and launch the SKUD-A (SS-1B) missile. This missile was in fact an Army ICBM deployed as an interim measure

owing to delays experienced with the production of the navalised ICBM – the SARK (SS-N-4).

At the same time as the 'Z' class vessels were being adapted to carry ICBM's an interim development of the Intermediate Range Ballistic Missile (IRBM) was planned for fitting to a small number of 'W' class vessels. The plan was for these vessels to test a number of configurations of the launcher and to test new launch systems and also to explore the potentials of the SHADDOCK (the IRBM in question) under operational conditions. It was soon found that the SHADDOCK required at this stage of its development extra mid-course guidance, and so an almost equal number of 'W' class submarines were taken in hand to those under conversion to missile carriers, and converted into radar guidance vessels, a conversion which was completed about the end of the 1950's.

While units of the 'W' and 'Z' class were undergoing conversion to missile carriers an improved version of the 'Z' class was under development as an attack submarine. Following the failure to perfect the Walter turbine, and with a nuclear power unit under development, the new 'F' class ocean going submarines (radius 20,000nm) reverted to diesel/electric propulsion. It was planned that these high speed submarines would replace the now obsolescent vessels of the 'W' class, and that production would run parallel with the atomic powered submarines until the latter had proved themselves in service. With the availability of the nuclear armed torpedo a very large programme of construction of over 50 boats was embarked upon. This entailed a rethink as to the tasks which these vessels were to perform. Instead of working on the basis of attacking enemy warships at sea, as hitherto, it was decided to employ the new class with its deadly nuclear armed torpedo to attack enemy ports and anchorages where far greater destruction from the use of the weapon could ensue.

When Kruschev became Premier of the Soviet Union in March 1958 a new naval policy emerged. By now the Russians had perfected the nuclear reactor to the stage where it could be mounted in a ship, and the icebreaker *Lenin* was at sea with a primitive type of reactor. With a propulsion unit that gave so many advantages Kruschev at once set about planning Russian naval strategy with the emphasis placed on the nuclear submarine. As a result all other design developments were cancelled, delayed, or subordinated to the overriding need to construct as quickly as possible nuclear-powered submarines. It was in fact only with the greatest difficulty that Kruschev was dissuaded from almost completely scrapping the surface fleet. While the *Lenin* was at sea proving the nuclear reactor a whole new fleet of nuclear submarines was under construction having all the advantages of range, power and speed and being capable of operating the new ICBMs and IRBMs then under development and undergoing trials in converted submarines.

As the trials with the ICBMs on the converted 'Z' class – the 'ZVs' neared completion, the 'G' class began to enter service with the Fleet. Unfortunately delays occurred with the completion of this class, mainly as a result of problems with the missile and its launch system which like the IRBM had to be launched from the surface. In fact the first few boats completed were armed with the SKUD-A missile which had in fact been tested and used to test launch apparatus in the 'ZVs'. The problems were overcome at a later stage and the vessels were able to operate the surface launched SS-N-4 SARK, as designed, while in 1964 some vessels were further modified to operate the third generation of IRBMs, the SS-N-5 SERB which could be launched underwater. The delays experienced with this class and the associated problems with the missile system, finally led to a curtailment of the construction programme so that in the end no more than 30 boats were built.

By this time the tactical duties for which the IRBM had been originally developed were abandoned and a new strategy became apparent. The original concept of the employment of the missile was in the bombardment of the coastal cities of America, but this idea was abandoned (principally because an ICBM – the SARK with a range of about 380 miles – was then in production) and the

missile was put to use in an anti-surface vessel mode. The 'W' class, as already mentioned, experimented with three different configurations for the IRBM launcher in an endeavour to overcome problems with the equipment, the most serious of which forced the submarine to have to surface in order to carry out a launch. The three configurations tried were firstly a single cylinder sited aft of the conning tower. This was an almost identical system to that used by the Americans on board the USS *Tunny*. To launch the missile the cylinder was elevated to about 25 degrees and the missile launched over the stern of the submarine. Trials with the system commenced about 1956 and were soon followed by a conversion fitted with two launching tubes sited immediately behind the conning tower and recessed into the hull. As with the single cylinder conversion these tubes were elevated to about 25 degrees for firing, which had to be carried out on the surface. Severe hydrodynamic problems were encountered as a result of these massive protuberances, not the least of the problems being that of cavitation giving rise to such turbulent conditions in the water that the risk of detection was enormously increased. The third conversion of the 'W' class (the Long-Bin), carried out in about 1960, was an attempt to overcome the problem of cavitation, and also to solve the problem of dispersal of the exhaust gases formed when the rocket was fired. In this configuration two superimposed launchers sited either side of the conning tower and built into the lengthened midships structure were fixed at an angle of about 14 degrees, and fitted with apparatus to absorb these gases. Problems were still encountered, however, and the submarines were still forced to surface to carry out a launching.

In the end it was decided to adopt the configuration tested in the 'W' twin cylinder class, but with certain modifications, and a new class of submarines to operate the SHADDOCK missile was designed, construction running parallel to the Long-Bin conversions. As a result the planned conversion programme of the 'W' class was severely curtailed, only six instead of 72 units being converted. The new class – the 'J' – were designed as conventionally powered boats and a total of 72 vessels was planned (to take the place of the planned 'W' conversions now cancelled). However, due to a number of problems, again the major one being that the vessels were forced to surface in order to launch their missiles and secondly the impractical nature of the launching cylinder (whilst cruising the cylinder lies horizontal retracted into the submarine hull. To launch the missile a hatch is opened at the after end of the cylinder, of which there are two pairs, one forward and one aft of the conning tower; the cylinder is then elevated to about 30 degrees before launch takes place) only 18 units of this class were finally completed. It also became apparent to the Soviets at this time that apart from a completely unsatisfactory launch system the missile itself was obsolete in this role, for by the time it became fully operational about the middle 1960's the increased radius of action of American carrier aircraft enabled the carrier forces of the West to operate outside the range of the Russian shore based aircraft which were to provide a protective umbrella for these missile carrying submarines.

It was now imperative for the Soviets to design a new vessel capable of carrying out a subsurface launch of a missile with far greater range than the SHADDOCK. It was at once apparent that only part of this problem could be overcome, by the use of nuclear power, of which the first such powered submarines – the 'N' class – were at that time (1960) entering service. As an interim measure five nuclear powered boats of a new class – the 'E-1' – were designed, and as it appeared that no new tactical missile would be available for some years, the best was made of a bad situation and the 'E-1' design slightly modified to carry four twin SHADDOCK missile launchers, twenty such boats of the improved 'E-2' design being laid down. The launching system on the 'E' class submarines is almost identical to that on the 'J' class. The problem of having to surface to launch the missile remains, but the nuclear power plant gives the 'E' class a substantial advantage over the 'Js' in both radius of action and submerged speed. Little progress was made with the

development of the missile, and with the advent of the nuclear-powered attack submarine armed with nuclear armed torpedoes and long range ICBMs now under development, it now appears evident that development of the SHADDOCK for use in submarines has ceased: a fact that is further substantiated by what appears to be conversion back into attack submarines of a number of the 'E' class, and also by the fact that no further development of this type of submarine has appeared since the last of the 'E' class was completed in 1967.

While the 'J' and 'E' class were being developed a new class of conventionally powered attack submarines equipped with a highly efficient sonar set was designed and built. Mass production centres for this class – the 'R' – were set up and a total of 550 units had been planned, but with the 'N' class nuclear submarines under construction at the same time it was decided, with Kruschev's policy of a nuclear submarine fleet in mind, to curb construction of this class to 21 units to enable more effort to be put into the nuclear submarine programme, which was just beginning to get into its stride.

In 1959 the first of the new nuclear powered attack submarines – the 'N' – entered service, only four years after the first Russian nuclear powered vessel *Lenin*! This was indeed an incredibly short time in which to have developed a nuclear propulsion unit suitable for use in submarines and to have designed a submarine capable of fitting such a unit. Nor was this all, for in 1962 the 'N' class submarine *Leninsky Komsomol* made a highly publicised voyage under the North Polar ice cap and actually surfaced at the North Pole. In view of the navigational difficulties of voyaging under the Polar ice and the fact that the nuclear reactor proved itself under such severe operational conditions, it is obvious that much new technical equipment must have been developed and fitted to these submarines. For all this to have been accomplished in such a short space of time seems incredible, especially in view of some of the past performances concerning Russian technological advances in the naval field. It is fairly certain that much of this new equipment had as its origin Western counterparts, details of which would have been supplied by Russian agents. There is further convincing proof of this possibility in that the Russian sonar sets fitted in the vessels of the 'N' and subsequent classes, are all practically identical with those fitted in British submarines, details of which were given to the Russians by the Portland spy ring of Lonsdale, Houghton and Gee.

A large programme of construction was planned for the 'N' class, but in spite of the apparent success of the class there were, as usual, problems. It was obvious that due to excessive noise from the power plant many of the advantages to be gained from the new class would be lost, especially in view of the superiority of the A/S techniques of the West, their equipment and new nuclear powered hunter-killer submarines, some details of which the Russians had been able to acquire. Not only this, but the Soviets soon found other problems with the reactor. The first vessel of the class to be completed – the *Leninsky Komsomol* – underwent a three year period of tests and trials, a most unusual procedure in Russian research, design and development techniques, which procedures usually run in parallel. It could have been that the Russians had run into difficulties with their reactors and linkage systems. This theory might be born out by a number of factors such as the fact that only 15 vessels of this class were completed when construction suddenly appeared to cease. Further in April 1970 a submarine of the 'N' class was sighted in a disabled condition on the surface in the North Atlantic. She was low in the water and accompanied by two Soviet merchant ships which were attempting, unsuccessfully as it turned out, to tow the submarine in the heavy seas. Two days later the submarine sank leaving two oil slicks on the surface. This accident had been preceeded by another incident about two months previously when the inland shipyard of Gorki on the River Volga, which specialised in building large pre-fabricated submarine sections (probably those housing the reactor etc as it subsequently turns out), was rocked by an enormous explosion. There were a number of fatalities and the area, including the river,

was heavily polluted with radio-active waste.

In 1964 Premier Kruschev resigned from office and yet again there was a noticeable change in naval policy. For the previous seven years Russian warship effort had been concentrated on submarine development, and to Kruschev's lasting credit they had achieved the ability to operate a nuclear deterrent from a submarine (the SARK on the 'ZV' and 'G' class submarines) but to the detriment of surface warship construction. With what seemed to be a well equipped submarine arm with new vessels in many ways comparable to those in the West it was decided to concentrate over the next few years in building up the surface fleet with a large number of missile armed warships.

This shift in construction policy came about as a direct result of a fundamental change in Russian naval strategy. When Kruschev came to power in 1958 the official view regarding the navy was that it was in being purely to act in support of and to co-operate with land operations by the army. Russia was basically a continental power and her warriors were not by nature seamen. Under Kruschev the naval effort had been concentrated in putting the Russian nuclear deterrent to sea in submarines (it was indeed at sea, but in the 'ZV' and 'G' classes it was to all intents and purposes a negligable weapon for the SARK rockets had to be fired from a surfaced submarine). By 1964 even the Russian Army admitted that the main duty of the Navy was to seek combat with enemy forces in the *open sea* as well as in harbour and around the coastline. At long last the fundamental theory that the role of the Navy was to support the Army was dispelled. A whole new concept in naval operations was promulgated and was to evolve around an ocean strategy which would have five main aims:

(1) The deployment of a nuclear strategic force.
(2) Neutralisation of the West's carrier attack forces before they could launch their nuclear armed strike aircraft.
(3) Protection of the homeland against Polaris attacks, and protection of the trade routes leading to Russia.

Top: 'R' class patrol submarine developed from the 'W' class. This submarine carries an extremely efficient sonar set. It is powered by conventional motors developing a speed of 16 knots underwater./Official USN

Above: 'N' class submarine. There may well have been problems with this class. The vessel shown here was sighted disabled in the North Atlantic in April 1970 and was found later to have sunk./Official USN

Right: An 'H-II' class submarine in difficulties 700 miles west of Ireland. The H-II class submarine carries three SERB missiles instead of the obsolete SARK in the H-I class. It would appear that this submarine had also had trouble with her power plant./MoD, RN, Official

**(4)** Destruction of the enemy's trade routes.

**(5)** Maintenance of command of the coastal areas in the Baltic, Barents and Black Sea and the ability to deploy and support land forces in the area of the coast.

From the above points it is obvious that during Kruschev's regime naval policy was moving towards an ocean strategy, but with its power vested mainly in the submarine. Out of the five aims noted above, four of these relied heavily on submarines for their maintenance. In Point 1 there was a gradual shift of emphasis from the land based deterrent to the submarine operated deterrent based on the 'ZV' and 'G' classes. No 2 in part relied on the submarines of the 'W' and 'Z' classes, although they had by this time become obsolete as a result of A/S techniques in the West. It also relied in part on the IRBM's carried by the submarines of the 'J', 'E' and converted 'W' classes, although these too were obsolescent. Defence against the POLARIS was to be vested in the new generation of nuclear powered hunter killer submarines such as the 'N' class. Point 4 relied very heavily on the 50 vessels of the 'F' class while Point 5 in part relied on the submarines of the 'Q' and 'R' classes for defence in the coastal areas.

It was realised, however, that to rely purely on submarines for the execution of an oceanic policy was a very short sighted policy, especial policy was a very short sighted policy, especially in view of the superior capabilities of the A/S systems of the West. With the new strategy defined the Russians at once set about implementing the new policy, which was combined with a new political offensive in various strategic areas of the world. The main aim of the Russian Navy was nothing less than the complete domination of the oceans of the world in support of the political aims of the Soviet Union. Coupled with a strong policitcal initiative the Russians, with their new military might vested in a super modern navy, were in a position to overawe and intimidate many lesser countries around the world. Certain areas in particular came in for close attention from the Soviet Union. Among these areas were the trouble spots of

the world such as the Arab States of the Middle East, who were in conflict with Israel, the newly emerging African countries, and certain areas of the Carribean and Latin America that were ripe for subversion. In latter years the sub-continent of India and islands in the Indian Ocean and Persian Gulf have also come in for close attention from the Russians who wish to establish base facilities in these areas.

Russian naval squadrons have appeared in many places where Soviet warships have never been seen before, all of them engaged in showing the flag. Most of these squadrons have been composed of the new guided missile surface vessels and have been notable, in the majority of visits, for the almost complete absence of submarines. Exceptions have been a number of visits by submarines to Cuba, one or two visits made to ports in the Baltic and occasional submarine visits to North African ports. These political and naval manoeuvres are not always attended with success, however. The most notable example of a failure was the island of Cuba in the Caribbean, where the Russians had hoped to establish a missile base. Their moves were thwarted, but Castro is still able to extend visiting base facilities to the Russian Navy, although there is an unwritten agreement between Moscow and Washington that these will not include missile carrying nuclear submarines. Recently, however, this unwritten agreement has been violated when nuclear-powered missile carrying E-II type submarines have paid visits to Cuba. Submarine tenders have also been based in the island, a vital factor in the last one or two years when nuclear powered ballistic missile submarines of the 'Y' class have looked for somewhere to rest crews and replenish when returning from POLARIS patrols along the East Coast of America. The temporary base facilities provided by Cuba give the Russian Navy a perfect position from which to carry out their naval strategy, for the island lies astride the major trade routes of the world which pass through the Panama Canal between east and west, also from the very rich traffic coming up from the River Plate and the mineral deposits and meat products of South America and from where Russian submarines can dominate the sea traffic from the Texas oilfields.

This oceanic strategy was aimed partly at gaining safe access routes between the four widely separated areas of Russian naval influence in the Black Sea, Baltic, Pacific and Arctic.

Other moves met with mixed success. In East Africa the Russians were forestalled by the Chinese, but units of their Indian Ocean Squadron still pay visits to Kenya and Ethiopia for Navy Days, often anchoring alongside warships from Britain and other countries. Such is the importance paid to these 'showing the flag' visits that Princess Anne was invited aboard the destroyer *Skritinii* when it was present at the Ethiopian Navy Day celebrations in February 1973.

In the Mediterranean the Russians field a formidable force* including numerous submarines. Until 1972 Russian warships had the free use of a permanent base in Egypt, but these facilities were withdrawn in 1972 and the Russian Fleet is now only granted visiting facilities; so although the submarine tenders working with Russian warships in the Mediterranean can rest, replenish and carry out minor refits in their normal anchorages off Alexandria, the Gulfs of Sidra and Hammamet and off Crete and along the North African coast, any major overhaul or repair necessitates a passage back through the Dardanelles to the Black Sea.

In the Indian Ocean the Russian Navy suffered further setbacks in its efforts to establish a base in that area when a concession to the Kuwait Oil Company enabling them to set up an oil installation on the island of Mauritius was altered (it was to have been leased to Russia for refuelling purposes) and the trawler agreement between Russia and Mauritius stipulated that the Russians would not be allowed to use the island convertly as a 'base'. To some extent this loss may have been redeemed by the diplomatic moves to establish friendly relations with the new state of Bangladesh, the first move being

* See article on the Balance of Power in the Mediterranean.

the acquisition of the rights to get the ports in that country in working order again. Russian working parties are even now engaged in removing wrecks and obsctructions left over from the 1971 war and a contract has been obtained to build up the Bangladesh fishing fleet (an excellent chance to establish Russian ECM spy trawlers in that area to monitor warship movements and to assist in keeping an eye out for the POLARIS patrols undertaken by the West in that area.)

The latest submarine developments to become apparent in the Soviet Union show that in many ways the Russians have caught up, and in some cases overtaken the Navies of the West. Towards the end of the 1960s construction began of two new classes of attack submarines. The strength of the West's POLARIS fleet necessitated an effective counter to be operated by the Russian Fleet. They were unable to combat the West's submarines from their surface warships as they lack such refinements as variable depth sonar and dipping sonar, details of which the Portland Spy ring had been unable to give them. A primitive form of VDS was tried in the 'Moskva' class, but would appear to have been unsatisfactory in operation, a factor which may have influenced Soviet planners in a decision not to proceed with the construction of these vessels. A further factor would have been the lack of efficient dipping sonar sets that would have been carried by their helicopters. On the other hand, the details of the submarine mounted sonar enabled the Russians to rapidly provide a counter to the West's POLARIS fleet and has led directly to the introduction of the 'V' and 'A' classes. The nuclear-powered 'V' class was first laid down in the mid-sixties and so far 11 units have been identified. These submarines are a direct development of the 'N' class and it is presumed that they have overcome some of the problems associated with that class. Of far greater concern, however, is their submerged speed, which has been estimated as being in excess of 30 knots, which together with their excellent sonar and nuclear armed torpedoes makes them a formidable adversary to the West's POLARIS fleet. At present construction of the Russian POLARIS Fleet takes

*Above :* 'C' class submarine. The hull is 'tear-drop' shaped and there is a large bulbous bow housing the sonar and possibly missile guidance equipment./*Official USN*

*Below :* Russia's counter to the POLARIS submarine—the 'Y' class submarine deploying **16 SAWFLY ICBM** missiles./*Official USN*

precedence over all other construction and so only a relatively small number of these vessels have entered service, and the rate of construction is only running at about two per year.

Three other new classes of submarine have recently been observed in the Soviet Navy. One of these shows that over the last decade the Russians have made startling progress in a number of fields. Plans for the 'Y' class POLARIS type submarine were first drawn up in the early sixties. At the time, however, problems with the missile (SAWFLY) and its associated launch system precluded any possibility that construction could commence until the late 1960's. In the meantime construction centered on the conventionally powered 'G' class operating a surface launched missile of low range (SARK) and the nuclear-powered 'H' class operating at a later date an improved missile with greater range and subsurface launch capability. Final development of this missile, the SERB, led to the introduction of a true POLARIS type missile, the SAWFLY, with a range of about 1,750 miles.

With production of this missile underway it was possible to commence work on the construction of the 'Y' class. This class is practically identical to the American 'George Washington' class POLARIS submarines and was first reported as being in service in 1968, three to four years later than originally planned. To date 25 vessels of the 'Y' class have been observed with 10 more under construction. With this rate of construction the Soviet Union will have reached parity with the West by 1975 and the total number of ICBM submarines available to the Russians will be well above that of the West. However, some of these submarines will undoubtedly be deployed against targets in China, but even so the West now faces a formidable threat from this force. At the beginning of 1973 further reports were received of what appears to be a new type of Russian POLARIS missile. Reports circulating in the West state that in trials in the Pacific Ocean on November 27, 1972 the missile, the SSNX–8, achieved a phenomenal range of 4,000 miles. This is obviously the new generation POLARIS missile developed as a counter to the American POSEIDON/TRIDENT. No specific details are available concerning the missile, but it is quite probable that it will be retro-fitted to the 'Y' class, and that in addition a new class of submarine will be designed to operate the missile. This has now become a necessity as the early Russian missile submarines of the 'ZV', 'G' and 'H' classes are obsolete, although they will probably remain in service until they are no longer seaworthy.

The second new class, the 'B' class, appeared at the end of the sixties and although not yet certain, it seems as though this class is conventionally powered, a theory that is substantiated by the apparently small dimensions of the class. These submarines are obviously intended for coastal operations and presumably will replace the obsolete 'W' class and aging 'Q' and 'R' classes now used in this role, and numbers of which have lately been handed over to satellite countries.

The last class to appear, again about the end of 1969, was the nuclear-powered 'C' class. These appear to be a development of the tactical missile submarines, although they do not appear to be a direct development of the 'E' class. The 'C' class vessels have eight missile launchers, four to starboard and four to port, capable of launching short range tactical missiles, presumably anti-shipping weapons for use against convoys. It is possible, however, that these missiles are a type of weapon similar to the American SUBROC missile. This is an Underwater-to-Underwater missile whose flight path is taken through the atmosphere, rather than through the water like a conventional torpedo. It has already been hinted that such a weapon is under development by the Soviets, and it could well be that this is the type of missile carried by the 'C' class and which would give them formidable teeth in an anti-submarine role. At present there are only eight units of this class in service and the rate of construction has been pegged at about two per year.

At present the most important submarines under construction in the Soviet Union are the vessels of the 'Y' class, construction of all other classes being sublimated to this POLARIS programme. As the total nuclear powered submarine construction capability of the

Soviet Union is estimated at about 20 per year, and of this the 'Y' class consume about half, then no more than two vessels per year can be constructed of the 'A', 'B', 'C' and 'V' classes. It can therefore be assumed that when the present Soviet POLARIS programme has been completed in about three years time (when there should be about 50 'Y' class vessels operational) production will switch to a new generation of attack submarines, which type must be high on the list of Soviet warship priorities. There will probably be an expansion in the rate of construction of the 'V' class and also possibly of the 'C' or its derivative. In the meantime planning will forge ahead on a new class of POLARIS vessel to carry the new missile.

One aspect not so far covered in this article concerns that of manpower. This, of course, must remain very much a matter for conjecture. The shortcomings of World War II have already been noted, where attempts to compensate for lack of operation experience and technical knowledge were made by the use of captured German technicians. The Soviet Union relies on conscription to man its services and so they do not suffer from the shortage of manpower as is the case in some Western navies. Training, especially with regard to submarine crews, is especially rigid, but nothing can compensate for lack of successful operational war experience on which to base training, and in which, as has already been shown, the Russian Navy gave a poor performance during World War II. Neither can the Russians make up for lack of tradition, for, as Admiral Cunningham once put it, "it takes 300 years to build a tradition", and such naval tradition as the Russians once possessed has already been destroyed twice, by the Revolution, and by Stalin's purges. The submarine branch is now the *élite* arm of all the Soviet services and shore training for submarine crews, especially in the technical aspects, is of an extremely high standard. Long sea patrols are also undertaken now, and have built up a hard core of seamen, who must be regarded as highly experienced in handling submarines at sea. Their moral, psychological and physical condition in particular receives close attention. But although these factors count for a great deal, and are backed up by an evidently high morale, there is still the imponderable question as to how submarine commanders would react under war conditions and even more important, whether they would be allowed to exercise their initiative in the pursuance of operations. Let us hope that we are never forced to find out the answer to this question under practical conditions!

From the foregoing study it is obvious that the Soviets in the past have made mistakes, both in construction and development techniques, and sometimes too in strategical concepts. The quality of individual classes of submarine has varied greatly over the years, between the excellent designs of latter years with the correct strategical concepts for their employment, to the previously inadequate designs based on incorrect strategical ideas. In addition owing to the peculiarity of the Russian research, design and development system and its inherent problems, individual classes of submarine are often someway behind their Western counterpart. Thus in spite of a construction programme of ballistic missile submarines which far exceeds anything in the West, these submarines are already becoming obsolete following publication of certain details concerning the next generation of American missile submarines. Similarly the Russian attack submarines are now probably falling behind again in sonar techniques following the break-up of the Portland spy ring. In the field of missile development the Russians seem to have caught up with the West, especially with the news in February 1973 of the testing of a new 4,000 mile range submarine launched ICBM. This is obviously the successor to the SAWFLY. Development of submarine launched IRBM's appears to have finally ceased and effort is probably now being concentrated on development of a SUBROC type missile.

Thus it seems that Soviet submarines to some extent will nearly always lag behind those of the West, and in an effort to make up what is lost in quality the Russians will resort to sheer force of numbers to pose what is, obviously, the greatest threat faced by the West.

# Nuclear Frigates of the United States Navy

ANTHONY J. WATTS

Under the 1956 Fiscal Year shipbuilding programme the United States Navy ordered its third nuclear powered warship, the guided missile frigate *Bainbridge*. This vessel was the forerunner of a type of warship which has gained increasing importance in the United States Navy. Development of a suitable nuclear power plant began back in 1957 and from then to the time of commissioning it took just five years to complete the *Bainbridge*. With practically unlimited radius of action the *Bainbridge* was designed to provide A/A-A/S protection for the nuclear powered carrier *Enterprise* and the cruiser *Long Beach*. The design was a one-off conception and at that time (early 1960s) no further consideration had been given to the mass production of nuclear powered surface warships, although

tentative plans had been put forward for a second nuclear carrier.

Under the 1962 Fiscal Year programme the United States Navy ordered seven oil-burning frigates, but Congress, in spite of the astronomical cost of the three previous nuclear powered surface vessels ($947,760,000) stipulated that one of the seven frigates should be nuclear powered. This vessel, the *Truxtun*, was fitted with an identical nuclear power plant to the *Bainbridge* and was similar in many ways to the earlier nuclear frigate. When the *Truxtun* was commissioned in May 1967 she was equipped to perform a similar A/A-A/S function to the *Bainbridge*, but mounted only a single twin TERRIER Surface-to-air missile launcher instead of the two twin mounts in the *Bainbridge*. In addition the TERRIER launcher on the *Truxtun* was dual purpose, being capable of launching either a TERRIER missile or an A/S ASROC missile. This presents the vessel with a certain disadvantage in that she can only engage one type of target at a time with her missile outfit, instead of the combination of targets that the *Bainbridge* can engage with her separate

*USS Bainbridge*, the world's first nuclear powered guided missile frigate./*Courtesy Bethlehem Steel*

Above: Nuclear-powered guided missile frigate *Truxtun*. Note the massive mast structure needed to support the radar aerials./*Official USN*

Left: The launching of the frigate *California* on September 22, 1971./*Official USN*

Below: Sketch showing the proposed layout of the 'Virginia' class frigates./*Courtesy Newport News*

TERRIER and ASROC launchers. Both vessels are, however, fitted with A/S torpedo tubes and have facilities for handling helicopters.

The cruiser *Long Beach* was originally projected as a large frigate. In 1956, however, it was decided that she should be given increased displacement to carry an extra TERRIER missile launcher. Following the success of the *Truxtun* and *Bainbridge* designs it has been decided that no more nuclear vessels the size of the *Long Beach* will be constructed, for *Truxtun* and *Bainbridge* can each perform perfectly adequately any tasks that may be assigned to the *Long Beach*. Thus, when it was decided to design and order a new class of nuclear carrier (the 'Nimitz' class) in 1967, the escorts to accompany the new carriers were planned as nuclear frigates of advanced *Truxtun* design. The nuclear power plant employed in the new nuclear frigates will be identical to that in the *Truxtun*, but radar, weapons etc, will be greatly improved and be of much greater sophistication.

The first of the new series of nuclear frigates – the *California* – was ordered under the 1967 Fiscal Year, and there were to have been a total of three vessels in the class. Owing to escalating costs, however, authorisation for the third vessel has been deferred. The 'California' class vessels have been designed as multi-purpose type warships to operate with fast carrier task forces. The intention was that with their much greater fire power and unlimited radius of action these vessels could replace the large number of older, less well-armed escorts at present needed to protect the carrier task forces. In addition the present gradual run-down of the American carrier fleet (by 1980 only 12 carriers will remain operational) means that fewer escorts of such sophistication will be required, and in addition the fewer escorts needed to cover a carrier task force means that the force as a whole presents a much smaller target to an enemy able to launch a variety of forms of attack.

In the 1970 Fiscal Year Programme the first of a further class of eight nuclear frigates was ordered. These vessels – the 'Virginia' class – have been designed primarily to perform escort duties to the three nuclear carriers of the 'Nimitz' class. However, two of the vessels planned for the 1973 Fiscal Year will not now be built because of increasing costs, and the authorisation of the remaining three vessels must almost certainly now be in doubt as well. The vessels of the 'Virginia' class (DLG(N) 38) are very similar to the vessels of the 'California' class. The main difference will be in the improved Anti-Air-Warfare (AAW) capability, A/S fire control system and the Combat Information Centre (CIC).

| Name | Displacement (standard) | Dimensions Length (oa) × beam × draught | Armament | Speed (knots) | Cost ($) |
|------|------------------------|-----------------------------------------|----------|---------------|----------|
| *Bainbridge* | 7,600 | 565 × 58 × 29 | 4–3in, 1 Asroc (8 barrel), 6 TT (2 × 3), 4 Terrier Launchers (2 × 2) | 30+ | 163,610,000 |
| *Truxtun* | 8,200 | 564 × 58 × 31 | 1-5in, 2-3in, 4 TT, Terrier/Asroc launcher (1 × 2) | 30+ | 138,667,000 |
| *California* | 10,000 (full load) | 596 × 61 × ? | 2-5in, ?-TT, 1 Asroc (8 barrel), 2 Tartar launchers (2 × 1) | 30+ | 200,000,000 (estimated) |
| *Virginia* | 10,000 (full load) | 585 × 63 × ? | 2-5in, 4 Tartar/ Asroc launchers (2 × 2) | 30+ | 222,000,000 (estimated) |

# The Balance of Power in the Mediterranean

## JOHN MARRIOTT

To assess the balance of power in the Mediterranean it is necessary to look at the whole picture of southern Europe. The Mediterrancan constitutes NATO's southern flank, what Churchill would have called its 'soft under belly', and it is on the flanks of NATO that Soviet pressure is most likely to be exerted.

First then let us glance at the map and see how NATO is situated geographically to oppose a possible Soviet attack. The East/West frontier extends from the Resia Pass in northern Ialy, along the northern border of Greece and Turkey, to Mount Ararat in eastern Turkey. Whilst certain sectors of northern Italy and eastern Turkey would be relatively easy to defend, the overall characteristics of the southern region place it in the difficult-to-defend category.

The area is composed of long peninsulars, projecting into the sea, or alternatively of long arms of the sea reaching far inland. These long projections of sea and land severely complicate the problem of logistics and communications, and preclude the establishment by NATO of a continuous line of defence.

It follows that the Mediterranean is a most important factor. Without control of the sea, supply of the land fighting forces would be seriously hampered. Loss of the sea would mean exposure of the land forces to attack on many varied and unpredictable fronts. Conversely, control of the Mediterranean denies its use to an enemy trying to outflank NATO forces in central Europe and permits its exploitation in carrying the attack to the enemy.

The Soviets have three principal avenues of land approach to NATO's southern area, all of which lack defensive depth on soil under NATO control. They are: through the pass at Gorizia to the Friuli Plain and the Po valley of Italy, through Austria across the Italian Alpine passes, and through the Vardar and Monastir Gaps in the mountains of northern Greece.

In all these cases the nearness of the sea to possible areas of combat makes protection of the sea lines of communication a matter of paramount importance. Loss of control of the sea would permit the Soviets to isolate and conquer the separate areas of the southern region.

From the purely naval point of view there are only two entrances to the Mediterranean (if one discounts the Suez Canal) – through the Turkish Straits and through the Straits of Gibraltar. At present both are dominated by NATO nations.

If Russia intended to carry out any form of maritime war in the Mediterranean she would have to secure the Bosphorous and the Dardanelles at one end and Gibralter at the other. It follows that these two gateways are vital to NATO. To defend the Turkish Straits it is obvious that the plains of Turkish Thrace, easily approached from Bulgaria, must be strongly defended. To keep control of the Straits of Gibralter it is, of course, essential that Britain should maintain her hold on Gibraltar, hence Britain's uncompromising attitude to Spain on this particular problem. In addition powerful naval forces would be required to patrol the Straits.

That then is a brief outline of the position in which NATO finds itself. Now let us look at the relative naval strengths of the opposing forces in this area which is so vital to either side.

### Soviet Forces

Any review of strength must necessarily be based on numbers, but it must not be forgotten that history has shown that often the numbers of ships, aircraft and men are far less important than their weapons and equipment and, above all, the morale and fighting spirit of the men. Since these two latter are impossible to estimate, we are left

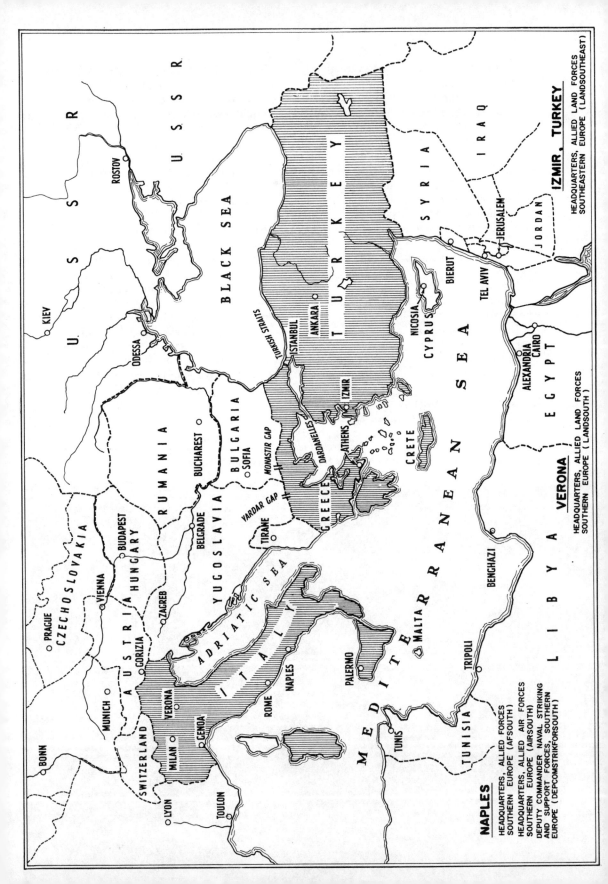

**NAPLES**

HEADQUARTERS, ALLIED FORCES
SOUTHERN EUROPE (AFSOUTH)

HEADQUARTERS, ALLIED AIR FORCES
SOUTHERN EUROPE (AIRSOUTH)

DEPUTY COMMANDER NAVAL STRIKING
AND SUPPORT FORCES, SOUTHERN
EUROPE (DEPCOMSTRIKFORSOUTH)

**VERONA**

HEADQUARTERS, ALLIED LAND FORCES
SOUTHERN EUROPE (LANDSOUTH)

**IZMIR, TURKEY**

HEADQUARTERS, ALLIED LAND FORCES
SOUTHEASTERN EUROPE (LANDSOUTHEAST)

with numbers, unsatisfactory though they may be.

That the control of the Mediterranean is vital to NATO is fully understood by the Soviets and for the past few years they have been showing, clearly and unmistakably, that, when the time comes, they would be prepared to challenge this control. The Soviet Mediterranean Squadron in peacetime consists of some 50 ships and submarines. The actual numbers vary considerably and may often exceed 50 as new units arrive to relieve ones about to return.

A typical breakdown of the squadron might be:

5 Destroyers of which 3 or 4 might be armed with guided missiles.
2 smaller destroyers.
2 or 3 amphibious ships
20 auxiliaries.
14 to 16 submarines.

It will be noted that the number of combatant vessels is only just over half of the total and of course they are far outnumbered by the combined NATO strength in the area (see the table on page 57). However the Soviets

have shown that they can greatly increase the numbers of ships and it is not beyond the bounds of possibility that at any time they might assemble a much larger fleet on the grounds of carrying out exercises. Even so, it seems unlikely that, at the commencement of hostilities, their total naval strength would exceed that of NATO's and, of course, at present they have no carriers to match the powerful Sixth Fleet.

**Air Power**

Up until recently the Soviets had a number of air bases in Egypt, but at the time of writing President Sadat has closed most of them down. Whether he will ever allow the Soviets back into Egypt is anybody's guess. In the meantime the Russians are now trying to establish themselves in Syria and it may be that eventually they will have a number of air bases there.

But air bases in the eastern Mediterranean are a long way from the Straits of Gibraltar,

American carriers of the Sixth Fleet on the occasion of the Fleet's twentieth anniversary in the Mediterranean.

through which all allied reinforcements for the area must pass, and so for some time now the Russians have been casting greedy eyes at possible bases on the North African littoral. As time goes on we may well see Soviet airfields in Algeria, Tunisia and Libia.

A powerful Soviet air strike force assembled along the shores of North Africa would pose a tremendous problem to NATO shipping in the Mediterranean. For example merchant shipping entering the Mediterranean from the Atlantic would have to be routed along the Spanish, French and Italian coasts, instead of proceeding directly through the centre, in order to put as great a distance as possible between them and the hostile airfields – a time consuming process.

Quite apart from the airfields, there seems little doubt that the Russians are building at least one carrier capable of operating fixed wing aircraft. It is probable that at this stage it is intended primarily for training, but in the years to come we may have to face the fact that Russian carriers may be operating in the Mediterranean just as freely as those of the Sixth Fleet.

## The Submarine Threat

With upwards of 16 Soviet submarines already in the Mediterranean, and with the possibility that many more might be deployed there before hostilities began, the threat of submarine attack is very great indeed.*

The greatest menace is undoubtedly the missile firing submarine. At present the Soviets do not have many of them, but the numbers are increasing daily, which is not surprising since they are undoubtedly the most formidable naval weapon to have been produced since the war.

The missile's range has been variously estimated from 150 to 25 miles, but, whatever it is, there seems no doubt that it can be fired from outside the sonar range of the normal anti-submarine screen and can be fired from a fully submerged position, probably on information obtained by hydrophones. The missile itself is believed to be

* See also article on Russian submarines by A. J. Watts.

capable of homing onto the target, by active radar means. Admiral Kidd, when he was the Commander of the Sixth Fleet, always said that he considered it to be by far the greatest threat to his fleet.

## Ships and Weapons

The types of Soviet ships seen in the Mediterranean are highly sophisticated and very modern. The two helicopter carriers, *Moskva* and *Leningrad* have often been seen and many of the destroyers have been armed with SHADDOCK, a large ship-to-ship missile with a range variously estimated from 150 to 400 miles. In the Mediterranean, because of its relatively small geographical size, it is thought that the missile would not be fired outside a range of 150 miles. Even so, some form of mid-course guidance would be required, probably an aircraft which would have to place itself in a position where it had the enemy ship(s) on its radar. Such a position would not be easily maintained in the presence of a carrier with fighter aircraft, or of a ship with long range Ship-to-air missiles. The threat from SHADDOCK is not therefore taken too seriously, except as a pre-emptive strike weapon. It might, for example, be fired before war was declared and be guided by a shadowing intelligence trawler, one of which is nearly always present with major NATO ships.

Recently a smaller guided missile destroyer has been observed with a different type of Ship-to-ship missile. It is smaller than SHADDOCK and is carried in a launcher mounted forward. It is possible that the missile is more comparable with the French EXOCET with a horizon range only.

Apart from destroyers the Soviets have a number of patrol craft equipped with the STYX missile (or its derivative) with a range of 14 to 20 miles, but few of these ships are seen in the Mediterranean nowadays.

For many years western observers have had doubts about the Russian's seamanship. Various near and actual collisions between NATO and Russian ships seemed to indicate that the Russian captains had little idea of ship handling and it was known that the Russians favoured the astern (and easier) method of fuelling at sea.

*Above :* **A Soviet 'Kotlin' class destroyer refuelling using the astern method. The Russians have now abandoned this method in favour of the abeam method.**

*Below :* The new Soviet 'Krivak' class destroyer. Note the quadruple missile launcher forward; the missiles are thought to be of horizon range only./*MoD, RN, Official*

However things are changing. Nearly all Soviet fuelling at sea is now done by the alongside method and, since President Nixon's visit to Moscow, the harassing of NATO ships has ceased (although this does not prove that the Russian seamanship has improved).

How the, apparently, very sophisticated Russian equipment performs in service and how well it is controlled is hard to estimate, but it would be foolish to underestimate it.

## NATO Strength

So much for the potential enemy. Now let us look and see whether our own house is in order.

NATO's southern flank is under the command of an allied Commander-in-Chief (CINCSOUTH), based at Bagnoli, a suburb of Naples. He has under him a Commander Land Forces (COMLANDSOUTH), a Commander Air Forces (COMAIRSOUTH) and a Commander Naval Forces (COMNAV-SOUTH). The latter used to be based in Malta, but because of Mr Mintoff's antics was moved to Naples in 1971.

COMNAVSOUTH, usually an Italian Admiral, has no forces under him in peacetime, but each Mediterranean country, plus America and Britain, make available certain naval and maritime air forces for exercises and in times of stress or war.

Reporting to COMNAVSOUTH is another command, set up in 1968, called COMAR-AIRMED, also situated in Naples, who is responsible for all maritime air reconnaissance. The commander is usually an American Admiral and his task is to coordinate all the maritime airborne activities of all the NATO nations in the Mediterranean.

There is one other important naval command in the area – the American Sixth Fleet. In peace the fleet has no NATO role, but of course takes part in exercises with NATO ships. In war, however, it comes directly under CINCSOUTH and changes its name to STRIKFORSOUTH. In peace, to keep the NATO side going, the Sixth Fleet Commander keeps a deputy in Naples, whose job it is to liaise with CINCSOUTH.

In war the maritime strength of all the NATO countries bordering the Mediterranean would be almost totally committed to NATO. In addition America and Britain would send what they could spare, dependent upon what is happening in the Atlantic. France would presumably come in on the side of NATO, but she also would have to divide her maritime strength between the Atlantic and the Mediterranean. The Sixth Fleet, as mentioned above, would also be committed to NATO.

The table on page 57 shows the estimated strength of the opposing forces at the outbreak of war, but it is stressed that it is only an estimate, as it is impossible to forecast exactly what forces would be in the area at the crucial moment.

The NATO forces shown are, however, already in the Mediterranean (beginning 1973) and it will be seen that they greatly exceed in numbers the strength of the average Soviet squadron in the area.

Although NATO predominates in numbers, it is lacking in modern equipment. For example the majority of NATO ships are around ten or more years old, whereas the Soviet ships are generally less than five years old. Few NATO ships are armed with Ship-to-air long range missiles and only a few Greek patrol boats at present carry Ship-to-ship missiles, although this will be rectified in the next year or two when EXOCET and OTOMAT come into service. Neither of these missiles has anything like the range of the Soviet SHADDOCK.

In peacetime ships of the NATO countries only get together for exercises. The Soviet ships work together all the time. There is a NATO 'on call' Mediterranean Standing Force of destroyers and frigates, but unlike its Atlantic counterpart, it is only activated occasionally.

However, there is one powerful force which works together all the time – the US Sixth Fleet. It is made up of some 40 ships, 175 aircraft and is manned by 21,000 officers and men. It consists of the following:

● 2 Strike carriers.
● 2 guided missile cruisers, of which one is the fleet flagship.

- About 20 destroyers (some of which are GM destroyers).
- A squadron of attack transports and cargo ships.
- A variety of amphibious assault craft.
- Auxiliaries, tankers, provision ships etc.

The fleet is organised in three main task forces. TF 60 consisting of the carriers, cruisers and about 12 destroyers; TF 61 consisting of the amphibious force with 1,500 to 2,000 marines embarked; TF 63 consisting of auxiliaries.

With the exception of the fleet flagship and one destroyer squadron, all ships do about six months in the Mediterranean, rotating with others from the American east coast. The flagship remains on station and uses Gaeta, just south of Rome, as her home port, whilst the destroyer squadron uses Athens.

In peace the fleet's main task is to deter aggression and it does this very effectively by cruising the Mediterranean year in and year out, showing the flag and always ready for any emergency.

The carrier task force operates with the two carriers separated by up to 200 miles. It is considered that to operate both of them in close company would provide too tempting a target for a pre-emptive Soviet strike.

In general, one carrier keeps to the western Mediterranean and the other to the central; neither goes into the eastern Mediterranean unless the political situation demands it. The reasons for this is that there is far too much civil air traffic over the eastern Mediterranean and it would be dangerous to operate carrier borne aircraft.

The amphibious force operates separately and carries out practice landings in practically every NATO country.

The fleet used to spend about 70 per cent of its time at sea and 30 per cent in harbour, but this proved very expensive on fuel, so it now spends equal time at sea and in harbour – a procedure not very popular amongst the aviators who state that too much harbour time 'puts their eye out'.

It is the fleet's proud boast that they do not need to go into port; all refuelling, ammunitioning etc, is done at sea. When at sea the crews work extremely hard, flying takes place around the clock and there are constant exercises. In fact the fleet is virtually on a war footing.

The fleet's striking power is enormous. Each carrier has some 90 aircraft onboard, many of them strike aircraft which can be armed with nuclear bombs. Others include fighter/interceptors, reconnaissance, AEW aircraft and ASW helicopters.

The role of the Sixth Fleet in war is primarily to support the land battle. It is envisaged that their nuclear bombers would be able to strike right into the heart of southern Russia. However with the large Soviet presence in the Mediterranean this role is having to be slightly modified, in that the Sixth Fleet must first ensure its own security by knocking out potential Soviet threats. These may be guided missiles from surface ships or submarines, or they may be aircraft from North African airfields. It follows therefore that the NATO land forces cannot expect to be able to call on the Sixth Fleet at will, for they may be otherwise engaged.

As mentioned above, undoubtedly the greatest threat to the fleet is the submarine launched missile. A Soviet submarine, acting on reports from shadowing aircraft, or more likely by using her electronic intercept equipment, could get into a position ahead of one of the carriers. Then, when still outside sonar range from the carrier's screen, the submarine could fire her missiles in the general direction of the carrier, knowing that even if the direction was not quite right the missile would search for the target and then home.

The fleet cannot operate without the use of radar and sonar, the former could be intercepted by shadowing aircraft outside radar range from the fleet, and the latter could be intercepted by the submarine herself. Indeed, even if the fleet kept sonar silence, a large number of ships steaming around the ocean at high speed make quite enough noise in the water for a submarine to be able to identify their position fairly accurately by means of her hydrophones.

Detection of submarines is always difficult, but in the Mediterranean it is doubly so because sonar conditions are extremely bad, particularly in summer, and the detection range by active sonar is very limited. The Americans are making every effort to improve matters and, whilst some form of fixed sonar barrier might be placed across focal points, such as the Sicilian Straits, it is difficult to see how the missile firing submarine could be detected before she fires her missile.

## Maritime Reconnaissance

Largely because of the submarine menace, NATO is making strenuous efforts to ensure that no corner of the Mediterranean Sea is left uncovered from the air.

All the Mediterranean NATO countries, except Turkey, operate maritime aircraft. Italy uses Trackers, now being replaced by Atlantics. Greece uses Albatrosses. The Americans have Orions deployed in Sicily and at Rota in Spain and the British have Nimrods, based on Malta. All are coordinated by COMARAIRMED.

At least some of the aircraft are on patrol every day and they report all Soviet shipping sighted or detected. Reports are passed to COMNAVSOUTH in Naples, where a complete plot of all Soviet shipping in the Mediterranean is maintained.

The plot not only receives information from the air but from many other sources, both covert and overt. The plot also disseminates information to all other interested allied commands. The Sixth Fleet flagship, for example, keeps a plot which is fed both from COMNAVSOUTH and from American national sources.

French maritime air also plays its part. There is a close liaison between the French maritime headquarters and COMARAIRMED and COMNAVSOUTH.

All in all there is very little that the Mediterranean naval commands do not know about Soviet activities in the area. All surface ships are continuously plotted, and an allied ship usually being detailed to follow the major Soviet warships. It is more difficult to keep tabs on the submarines, but the NATO authorities usually have a pretty good idea where most of the submarines are.

Even so the problem of submarine detection from the air has by no means been solved. As mentioned above, sonar conditions in the Mediterranean are very poor and this renders the primary means of airborne detection of submerged submarines – sonobuoys – very ineffective. Other methods, such as Magnetic Anomaly Detection, Diesel Exhaust Detection, and Infra-Red, are all of very limited range or in their infancy. The fact remains that unless a submarine shows a portion of herself above the sea, the chances of detecting her from the air are small indeed. Fortunately, in peacetime, the Soviet sub-

A Nimrod aircraft overflies the Soviet helicopter cruiser *Leningrad* in the Mediterranean./*MoD, RN, Official*

marines do surface occasionally and show snorts and periscopes, but whether their nuclear ones ever do is another matter.

## Helicopters

An urgent requirement, from the defence of shipping point of view, is more helicopters. The Sixth Fleet at one time occasionally had a helicopter carrier attached to it for short periods, but the Americans are short of ASW carriers and it is by no means certain that one would be available in the Mediterranean in any future war.

Realising this, the American Navy is putting more ASW aircraft into their attack carriers and is also making efforts to get a helicopter into every ship down to destroyer size, under what they call their LAMPS programme.* However, the programme is progressing only slowly and, although a few American ships in the Mediterranean may have helicopters by the beginning of 1975, the full programme will not be implemented for a further two years after that.

Many British and Italian ships carry ASW helicopters, but few are found in the Greek and Turkish navies.

## Attack Submarines

Undoubtedly the best way in which to fight a submarine is with another submarine. The Americans, therefore, are now increasing the number of nuclear attack submarines in the Mediterranean. A submarine depot ship is to be based at La Maddelena, off the north coast of Sardinia and the submarines will work from her.

## Radar

The Mediterranean is not well supplied with coastal radars. These can be of great value in detecting shipping, but would require co-operating aircraft to identify detections. These might be helicopters. A combination of radars and helicopters would help to ease the burden on the limited number of long range maritime aircraft available.

Whilst on the subject of radar, it is perhaps opportune to remark that there are very few

* See *Warships and Navies 1973* p. 127.

air surveillance radars bordering the Mediterranean which 'look' to the south. The new NADGE radar chain 'looks' almost exclusively to the east. Thus early warning of air attacks mounted from the North African coast airfields, whether directed against land targets or shipping, would be conspicuous by its absence. Efforts are being made to fill the gap.

## Convoys

This brings up the question of how allied shipping in the Mediterranean is to cope with air attacks in war. If one assumes a conventional war of some length, it will be necessary to pass a considerable amount of shipping through the area. At present it is planned to do so in convoys, but the possible establishment of Soviet air bases along the North African seaboard is causing no little concern to the convoy planners.

With practically the only carriers in the Mediterranean being fully occupied in their strike role with the Sixth Fleet, there will be little or no fighter cover for convoys from carriers. The only cover that could be provided would be from AIRSOUTH's forces based onshore in Italy, Greece and Turkey. This leaves the western Mediterranean wide open to air attack from North African airfields. Attacks on convoys can be made more difficult by routing them up the Spanish coast, across the Gulf of Lyons and down the western Italian coast, but even this route would not be outside the range of aircraft from North Africa.

Another point which is worrying naval officers is that, what few fighter aircraft exist, are not only based far from the convoy routes in the western area, but are under the control of AIRSOUTH whose primary role is to support the land battle. If the Soviets really are going to deploy maritime strike aircraft all along the North African coast, then there would appear to be a case for fighter protection aircraft for ships to be under naval control, even though they are based ashore.

If France comes in with NATO it would presumably be possible to base fighter aircraft in southern France. If Spain, too, came

*Above :* A Sikorsky Seabat helicopter onboard an Italian ship.

*Below :* Russian Badger aircraft. These aircraft frequently carry out long range maritime patrols over the Mediterranean./*MoD, RN, Official*

in on NATO's side the problem would be greatly simplified. The real solution, of course, is more aircraft carriers, or at least vessels capable of operating VTOL aircraft.

## Malta

A word must be said about Malta. NATO, in their bargaining with the Maltese premier Mr Mintoff, did their best to assert that the island was of little value to them. However they agreed to pay £14 million a year for its use, for, of course, it is of the utmost value to the allies – value because if they are there the Russians will not gain possession of it, and value because it is in a highly strategic position, straddling as it does the main trade route through the Mediterranean.

Britain now operates maritime patrol aircraft from the island on behalf of NATO and also keeps a Royal Marine Commando there, ready for any emergency. British ships may use the harbours and, in the event of war, Malta could be made into a fully fledged advanced operational base.

## The Future

Throughout history the Mediterranean has often played a vital part in European wars. There is no reason to believe that things would be different in the future.

If NATO wants to stop the gradual Soviet infiltration into this important area, it can only do so by a show of strength.

It is true the Sixth Fleet shows its fangs whenever and wherever it can, but this is not enough. The Sixth Fleet in peacetime is not part of NATO – it is American. What is required is a strong NATO force, cruising the length and breadth of the Mediterranean, and showing the flags of the allies, surmounted by the seldom seen NATO flag.

The present 'on call' Standing Naval Force Mediterranean consists only of a handful of frigates or destroyers. It is activated only for exercises and is nothing like strong enough to impress anybody. Ideally the force should consist of one carrier, two cruisers or large guided missile destroyers and eight frigates or destroyers. It should be activated all the time, although naturally the ships might have to be changed as necessary.

The carrier would have to be American, though there is no reason why the *Ark Royal* should not take her turn for the remaining few years of her life.

The force would visit as many ports in the Mediterranean as possible, and these should include ports in Egypt, Syria and Israel as well as NATO ports. The latter are important for it is just as necessary to impress on our own allied public that NATO is doing the job for which the alliance was formed as it is to impress non NATO countries with NATO's strength.

It would, of course, take part in exercises and if it is seen by Russian ships and submarines from time to time, so much the better.

Like all flag showing squadrons it would entertain in harbour, throw ships open to visitors, take part in competitive games against the local populace and might even be used for emergencies to provide aid to stricken earthquake or other disaster areas.

Such a force would not only create goodwill for NATO throughout the Mediterranean, but would also be an earnest of NATO's intentions should war ever come.

If it is impossible for the Americans to provide a third carrier in the Mediterranean, would it not be possible for the carrier task force of the Sixth Fleet to assume a NATO rather than a national role and for its escorts to be drawn from Britain, America, Italy, Greece and Turkey?

Such an idea should appeal to the Americans who find difficulty in providing all the escorts so far from home. It would also serve to underline the fact that America is just as much a part of NATO in the Mediterranean as are the other NATO nations.

There is one other point. European NATO having virtually no carriers of its own means the Mediterranean nations' destroyers and frigates are gaining little experience in working with carriers. If they could be employed as a screen for the American carriers, and rotate at intervals, the experience gained might prove invaluable in war; for who can say that, in the face of casualties, the Americans will always be able to provide a sufficient screen for its carriers in the Mediterranean.

Apart from this idea there are a number of

other things NATO and the Americans can do. An urgent requirement is for a submarine launched missile equivalent to that of the Russians. Both America and Britain have been talking of such a weapon for some years and possibly it is under development, but both countries have been dragging their feet on getting it into service.

The value of helicopters in ships has already been mentioned, but there seems to be no reason why there should not be many more shore based ones. The Sicilian narrows, through which all Soviet submarines must pass if they are to be deployed in the eastern Mediterranean, is an ideal bottle-neck for submarine hunting. ASW helicopters based in Sicily, Pantellaria and Malta would be invaluable. Without doubt the NATO planners have stated the same thing and the lack of helicopters is probably due to lack of money with which to provide them. It is an unfortunate fact that NATO is bedevilled by lack of funds which will only be provided if the politicians and public opinion are both convinced of their necessity.

Britain's contribution to the Mediterranean is pitiful. The Royal Navy keeps one or two destroyers or frigates in the area and others visit for a few weeks at a time for training. For centuries Britain maintained a powerful Mediterranean Fleet because she knew that a show of strength was the best way to ensure peace. It did not always work, but if war came the British presence in the Mediterranean was never found wanting. Nowadays Britain seems content to leave it all to the Americans, Italians, Greeks and Turks. She very nearly gave up Malta altogether, leaving it wide open to the Soviets to rush in. Fortunately this has been staved off for a while, but if Britain wants to keep her hold on Malta what better way of doing it than by basing as many ships there as possible.

Once again it is a question of money. Britain has just not got the ships, but even so it does not seem impossible to establish, say, a working up and ASW training base there, rather as is done at Portland, and to rotate ships from Britain to Malta far more frequently than is done at present.

If the Suez Canal should re-open the num-ber of British merchant ships passing through the Mediterranean would probably double overnight. Is the Royal Navy not going to provide some form of protection for them in the Mediterranean against sudden emergencies?

If NATO wants to ensure its southern flank against sudden attacks, it must increase its strength in the Mediterranean now. It is no use leaving the protection of the Mediterranean to the NATO countries bordering it. NATO's southern flank is just as important to Britain, Germany, Holland and Belgium as it is to Italy, Greece and Turkey.

**NATO and Soviet Forces in the Mediterranean**

| | | Soviet | |
| | | Black Sea (including Med squad) | Typical strength of Med squad |
| Category | Nato | | |
| --- | --- | --- | --- |
| Attack Carriers | 2 | — | — |
| Helicopter Carriers | — | 2 | 1 to 2 |
| Surface Attack cruisers and destroyers | 5 | 5 | 2 to 3 |
| A/S destroyers, frigates, escorts | 66 | 57 | 5 to 9 |
| Patrol Boats | 9 | 31 | 0 to 4 |
| Submarines Nuclear attack | 2 | 4 | 2 to 3 |
| Missile firing | — | 4 | 2 |
| Diesel | 35 | 34 | 8 to 12 |
| Short Range | — | 10 | — |

*Notes*

(a) Above figures do not include the French Navy. On the assumption that half the total French naval force would be deployed in the Mediterranean, on the side of NATO, the allied strength could be increased as follows: Attack Carriers 1; ASW Carrier 1; Surface attack cruisers and destroyers 8; A/S destroyers, frigates, escorts 15; Attack S/Ms diesel 10.

(b) No account is taken of additional forces America and Britain might send to the Mediterranean in war.

(c) Numbers of maritime patrol aircraft in the Mediterranean vary, but at any one time there should be NATO 58; French 30 (approx).

57

# The Royal Navy in Alliance

## DESMOND WETTERN

Critics over the years since the war who have challenged successive governments on the continuing run-down of our naval power have almost always been given what now amounts to a political parrot cry: "In a future conflict we should not fight alone but with our allies in various treaty organisations".

Mr Healey, on the other hand, in excusing Labour's policy of total withdrawal from East of Suez claimed that this would result in our having "the largest navy in Western Europe". If, therefore, we mean to stress that as being one of the factors which makes us a valuable partner within the EEC we cannot, at the same time, go on cutting back the size of our naval forces and consequently on our commitments.

All those government spokesmen over the years, who have hidden behind the skirts of NATO and other treaty organisations, when challenged over our declining seapower forget one thing: any alliance is only as strong as the sum of its member's strength. If one member cuts back on its forces the strength of the whole declines.

In planning to withdraw our naval forces from East of Suez Mr Healey overlooked one vital point: from the point of view of many nations in Western Europe one of the most important contributions we could make to their security was the retention of at least some of our forces in the Indian Ocean. Like us, much of their trade and raw materials pass through important sea areas like the Straits of Hormuz at the mouth of the Persian Gulf; through the Malacca Straits and around the Cape of Good Hope.

If we did not provide at least a token to signify our intent to stay in the Indian Ocean there would be no other West European country with the capability of so doing. The 'little Englanders' of course argued that we had 'carried the can' for long enough and it was up to other nations to look after their own interests.

Such arguments conveniently overlooked the fact that in protecting our own interests we coincidentally safeguarded those of others. If one developed the 'little Englanders' argument to its logical conclusion one would end up with a host of minor powers all pursuing their own little policies until they were inevitably swallowed up by the Soviet Union.

In reversing the Labour East of Suez withdrawal policy the present British government evidently appreciated the importance to Europe of our forces' role *outside* the geographical sphere of influence usually held to be that of Western Europe. At the very least we should go on maintaining a presence in the Indian Ocean until recognition was won for extending NATO's area of responsibility beyond the Tropic of Cancer in the Atlantic.

This year saw the first step towards that goal with the cruise of an Anglo-Dutch squadron in the Indian Ocean and Far East. It was a small beginning but, as a former Supreme Allied Commander Atlantic, Admiral Ephraim Holmes USN, once pointed out to the writer: "The Russians suffer no inhibition at sea like that of NATO confined to the North Atlantic. In war these artificial limitations would be swept aside."

For NATO to revise its commitments to a point where it accepted world-wide responsibilities wherever Western security is involved is no doubt asking too much at this time when individual members have problems enough convincing their electorates to vote sufficient money to retain even existing forces and commitments. But at least NATO can be said to have shown cognisance of the fact that the maintenance of seapower is not something that can be forgotten once one is south of the Tropic of Cancer. Had we completed the East of Suez withdrawal of all our forces, as Labour had planned, it would certainly seem that the task of convincing our NATO partners in Europe that it was necessary to *create* a naval presence from scratch East of Suez would have been an uphill, if not impossible, task. It would doubtless have been pointed out to us that since only two years ago (ie 1971) despite the growing Russian squadron in the Indian Ocean, we had seen fit to withdraw our forces why were we now clamouring for the return of a multi-national force?

One of the greatest failings of many politicians is the idea that seapower is divisible; that ships can be deployed like battalions and one can opt out of one's commitments in one area in order to maintain others elsewhere. For a nation like Britain utterly dependent upon shipping for her very existence it is absurd to promote a policy that protects the path up the garden to the front door but ignores what is happening in the road outside. Thus our six frigates assigned East of Suez are just as important for NATO and our Common Market partners as are others in, say, the Standing Naval Force Atlantic.

RFA *Olna* transfers fuel to the American oiler *Neosho* in a NATO Exercise. In the background is the Canadian carrier *Bonaventure* refuelling from the *Olna* whose starboard side is covered with oil from a burst hose—a hazard of replenishment at sea./*Desmond Wettern*

Ironically, about the only ships we have which are not earmarked for NATO in time of crisis are the five patrol vessels in Hong Kong – yet the Colony has one third of our currency reserves without which we should be the 'poor man of Europe' with a vengeance. The permanent guardship at Hong Kong, HMS *Chichester*, is presumably in the same category.

The six frigates East of Suez include two based at Singapore and allocated as the British naval contribution to ANZUK, the combined tri-Service British, Australian and New Zealand force which replaced Britain's Far East Command in Singapore on November 1st, 1971. Although from time to time these two frigates put to sea on exercises with other Commonwealth units much of their time (usually three weeks for each ship) in Singapore is spent undergoing assisted maintenance. The Royal Navy also, with the Australian Navy, helps provide ANZUKS's submarine – the current British boat being *Odin* which is based at Sydney along with the Australian 'O' class submarines.

A curious feature of ANZUK is that despite its location in the middle of the South-East Asia Treaty Organisation's 'parish' there are no official links between the two. The reason

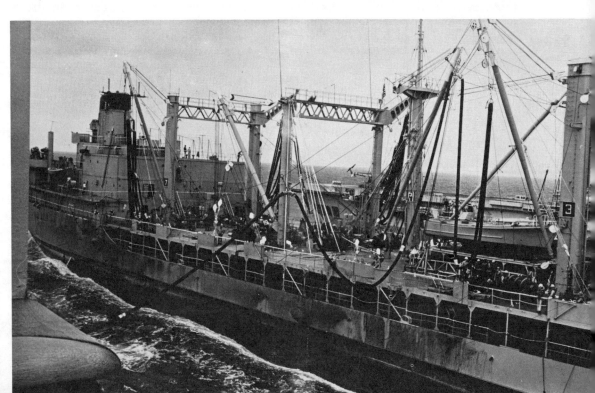

is Malaysia's unwillingness to be involved in any 'power bloc' which tends to polarize relations between East and West in the Malaysian Government's 'uncommitted' opinion.

Thus a curious situation can arise in which a British frigate is one day in ANZUK and the next is part of a SEATO exercise task force. Today one frigate is usually all that the Royal Navy can spare for SEATO exercises since there is not even a RFA assigned East of Suez on a permanent basis. But then there is only one major SEATO exercise in the course of each year.

One of the six frigates East of Suez spends about a third of the year in the Persian Gulf – on occasion even more than this. Usually one of these visits coincides with the annual Central Treaty Organisation naval exercise. Both SEATO and CENTO exercises, as well as the Navy's 'showing the flag' visits in the area, would benefit by the winding up of the Beira patrol as this would release a frigate for commitments elsewhere. In addition, to maintain a frigate continuously on patrol off the Mozambique coast requires six to be allocated to allow for refits, leave and time on passage.

Inevitably, with separation from wives and families now limited to a nine months' maximum there is a continual turn-over of HM Ships assigned East of Suez. This therefore means that considerable numbers still visit Simonstown for replenishment and maintenance.

A United States Navy C1A aircraft takes off from HMS *Ark Royal* during NATO Exercise Strong Express./*MoD, RN, Official*

Whenever possible these ships on passage exercise with South African naval and maritime air units in what are known as SANEX. These exercises help ensure that the South African naval forces are kept sufficiently abreast of the latest naval tactics to avoid any serious problems that might arise in time of war or emergency.

Across the South Atlantic there are occasional exercises with one or more South American navies. But these are infrequent and depend partly upon the availability of one of HM Ships in the area and also partly on whether a cruise by one or more British warships in this area would help sales of British warship designs and/or naval equipment. These irregular and widely spaced exercises have certainly proved their worth when it is recalled that warships for Argentina, Brazil, Chile and Peru are currently building or refitting in Britain.

Further north, the two frigates assigned to the West Indies squadron from time to time exercise with American warships in the area. In addition, the American anti-submarine centre at Key West, Florida, is used fairly frequently by British warships from the West Indies Squadron. But, as with exercises with South American navies, there is no question of any obligations arising from treaty requirements.

An agreement does, however, exist for the Atlantic Undersea Test and Evaluation Centre (AUTEC) at Andros island in the Bahamas. Completed in 1966 at a cost of some £42 million the Centre with the associated 40 mile long Tongue of the Ocean range running through the middle of the Bahamas is used to evaluate new anti-submarine weapons such as torpedoes, as well as new types of Sonar. It is also used for trials to reduce warships' hydrophonic effect.

Although primarily an American establishment there is a British naval liaison officer and from time to time HM Ships and RAF Nimrod aircraft make use of the facilities there. For any extensive trials British uniformed as well as scientific and technical staff are provided and a 'fee' is paid to the American Government, although Britain has been paying the annual interest on a 15-year £5 million loan Washington gave the Bahamas Government in return for the use of the site and mains services. The ill-fated submarine *Artemis*, which sank alongside the Gosport submarine base in 1971, was about to depart for trials with an RAF Nimrod at AUTEC. The RMAS torpedo firing ship *Whitehead* is also used on occasion in connection with experiments at AUTEC.

The foregoing outlines the Navy's principal commitments outside the European NATO area. Security at sea within the NATO area is clearly today the Navy's biggest commitment.

Broadly speaking, NATO naval commitments can be divided into three geographical areas, each with its particular conditions and requirements. These are: the North Atlantic; the Mediterranean and the 'Northern Flank' in the North and Norwegian Seas, Baltic and Arctic.

Britain's naval involvement in the Mediterranean in the course of this century has waxed and waned in approximately 10 year phases. Before 1914, when the Balkans occupied a place in world politics not unlike that of the Middle East today, the Royal Navy's Mediterranean Fleet was the premier and most sought after seagoing command. The rising power of the High Seas Fleet swung the emphasis back to northern European waters and the eventual formation of the Grand Fleet.

Crises in the 1920s in both Turkey and her former colonies once more put the emphasis of British seapower back in the Mediterranean and the rise of Mussolini resulted in this emphasis remaining in the inland sea up to the time of Munich. Throughout much of the last war, at least until the *Tirpitz* was severely crippled, the battlefleet was once more concentrated in northern waters.

After the war, although for reasons of manpower and money the Home Fleet remained the Navy's largest, the Mediterranean Fleet had the largest number of ships in *effective* commission. This was the case until the outbreak of the Korean War when the Mediterranean Fleet was denuded to build up the Far East Fleet.

The continuing demands in the Far East station until after the defeat of Indonesia's 'confrontation' against Malaysia in the 1960s meant that the Mediterranean Fleet was usually little more than a token force. But when the Russian Navy began to be a serious rival to the American Sixth Fleet British politicians seemed almost surprised that Washington should seek our greater involvement and evidently forgot how much 'the Med'. has featured in our naval history because of its strategic situation.

Today the *permanent* Royal Navy forces in the Mediterranean remain at a token level but it is being visited increasingly by a wide variety of ships. In the closing weeks of 1972, for example, an exercise with French ground forces in Corsica resulted in the presence of the *Ark Royal*, *Fearless* and *Intrepid*. An exercise in spring 1972 in the Eastern Mediterranean involved a Commando ship and Royal Marine Commandos.

For most of the time now a guided missile destroyer and usually two frigates are more or less permanently in the Mediterranean with supporting RFAs. Britain also contributes to the 'on-call' force which, for political reasons resulting from the age of the Greek and Turkish fleets, cannot yet be compared with the Standing Naval Force Atlantic. But at least the need for a cohesive naval policy among the NATO powers in the Mediterranean is now recognised by the politicians who are no longer entirely content to sit back and let the American Sixth Fleet bear the full burden of Western security at sea in the area.

The role of British naval forces along with those of Italy and to a lesser extent those of Greece and Turkey is primarily the defence of shipping and then defence of coastal areas against amphibious assaults. The main offensive capability is still vested in the Sixth Fleet.*

But since the Sixth Fleet is in the Mediterranean primarily to support American foreign policy the NATO planners evidently see a situation arising in which the Sixth Fleet's Marine Corps Battalion Landing Team

* See J. Marriott's article on 'The Balance of Power in the Mediterranean'.

might not be readily available to support a NATO commitment, or at least might be occupied elsewhere. For this reason the decision to keep two Commando ships and two assault ships in commission in the Royal Navy in order to have the capability of providing amphibious reinforcements on *both* the Northern and Southern flanks is welcomed.

One of the two frigates normally deployed in the Mediterranean is usually detailed for guardship duties at Gibraltar where, at most times, one frigate and one or two CMS are to be found under long refit. The purpose of the Gibraltar guardship is as much to keep track of Soviet naval movements in and out of the Straits as to be a deterrent to Franco's Navy. This latter task is more usually performed by an inshore minesweeper based at Gibraltar for the purpose.

Gibraltar is, of course, of great importance to the NATO navies as it has the only major dock available to warships of the Alliance in the Western Mediterranean. It also has important oil fuel storage facilities and an airfield which is the only one open to NATO aircraft west of Sardinia.

Elsewhere in the Mediterranean, there is a close link between the Underwater Weapons Establishment (UWE) at Portland, Dorset, and the NATO oceanographic research centre at La Spezia. The latter is concerned with, as a rule, basic scientific research, and its findings on such things as the seasonal distribution of thermoclimes are made available to establishments in the NATO countries such as UWE. There is a Royal Navy liaison officer on the staff at the La Spezia centre. Royal Navy officers and ratings also perform a variety of tasks at the Naples headquarters of the NATO Commander Southern Europe and there are Royal Navy officer students at the NATO Defence College in Rome.

Unlike the Southern flank, the Northern flank of NATO is less easily defined, although in NATO planning it covers the whole of Norway, Denmark and Schleswig-Holstein in northern Germany. It comes under the overall command of the Supreme Allied Commander Europe in Brussels with the Commander Allied Forces North (COMAF-NORTH) as subordinate commander with his headquarters at Kolsas outside Oslo.

Apart from providing COMAFNORTH himself and some of his senior staff officers and subordinate single Service commanders Britain has no direct involvement in the area. However, the Royal Navy's committal to the area is considerable.

Every year the one unit in Britain fully trained and equipped for Arctic warfare, 45 RM Commando, exercises with Norwegian and sometimes other NATO forces in the Tromso area in the far north. When available a Commando ship, amphibious assault ship or RFA-manned LSL bring the Commando and its supporting Fleet Air Arm Wessex V helicopter squadron to Norway.

Every three years NATO conducts a major exercise in which defence of the Northern flank is the primary task. The latest in this series of large-scale exercises, 'Strong Express', in the early autumn of 1972 involved *Ark Royal, Albion, Fearless* and *Blake* as well as considerable numbers of Royal Navy missile destroyers, frigates, submarines, MCM vessels, RFAs and anti-submarine helicopters operating from shore fields.

It is as well, at this stage, to look momentarily at the whole defence scene in north Norway in order to show how vital is the Royal Navy's role. For political reasons Norway has always forbidden the basing of foreign troops on her soil in peacetime. But although something like 350,000 men could be available within about 48 hours of general mobilisation the Norwegian regular forces are small and on the common frontier with the Soviet Union some 800 Norwegian troops face an estimated *peacetime* force of 20,000 Russians in the immediate border zone.

In winter aircraft and ships provide the only means of communication with southern Norway, but there are only four major military air bases in north Norway. It will therefore be appreciated that there could be unacceptable delays in mobilising and then moving Norwegian reserves to the far north.

Added to this the four airfields lack reliable radio communications because of the interference caused by the mountainous country and the Aurora Borealis (Northern Lights) at

Above: The after 6in gun turret of HMS *Tiger* used as a loading platform for a Dutch naval helicopter during a NATO exercise in 1962./*Desmond Wettern*

Below: An American Marine Corps CH-53 helicopter lifting a Land Rover from the deck of the commando ship HMS *Albion* during NATO Exercise Strong Express, September 1972./*MoD, RN, Official*

certain times of the year. The terrain also makes it difficult to provide adequate radar early warning and aircraft direction.

During 'Strong Express' the American Marines, with heavy-lift helicopters, put ashore 14 days before the exercise started a complex of radar aerials and satellite dish communications terminals on top of a mountain. It was considered that without this support there would have been grave problems in flying in transport planes bringing troop reinforcements from Germany and in directing the additional fighters also flown in.

But at a time of tension the setting up of this American radar and communications complex might well be seen as 'provocative' by Moscow and upsetting for a Norwegian Government protesting its lack of aggressive intentions towards the Soviet Union. If, on the other hand, such a complex were to be installed *after* Moscow had made a move it might well be too late.

In addition, it would presuppose that the necessary ships carrying the radio and radar equipment and the heavy-lift helicopters were already available in the Norwegian Sea or elsewhere nearby. Any Soviet aggression would almost certainly include pre-emptive strikes on the four northern Norwegian air bases.

It may, from this brief outline of the current defence situation in north Norway, be seen that NATO faces some grave problems. The answer must therefore be sought through the use of seapower.

Naval forces must be able to provide both air support and the means to put ashore at least sufficient troops to show Moscow that NATO as a whole would be involved pretty well from the start. The obvious way of achieving this would be to have a permanent force of carriers and amphibious ships in the area.

But the nearest NATO can afford to get to this in peacetime is the Standing Naval Force Atlantic. It is no coincidence that STANAVFORLANT frequently exercises in the Norwegian Sea to show Moscow that any aggression across the frontier into Norway would immediately involve the other NATO nations.

Britain does, of course, play her full part in STANAVFORLANT and in 1972 provided the first 'big ship' in the shape of the guided missile destroyer *Norfolk*. But the force has no amphibious or air support capability.

It would be easy to say that the NATO Strike Fleet could provide this. But even assuming the necessary ships were ready, their passage time from American East Coast ports would still be in the order of ten days. For this reason the Royal Navy now has a clearly defined new role; namely to 'hold the ring' until the Strike Fleet could arrive.

How this could be achieved if *Ark Royal* were under refit is far from clear and for this reason, if for none other, there must be more than one of the new Through-Deck Command Cruisers. Nevertheless, there is now a firm role for the Navy's big ships within the NATO framework despite all those who, in the past, have advocated the retention of anti-submarine forces to the exclusion of all others, particularly amphibious forces.

But both the Northern and Southern flanks of NATO become meaningless if control is lost of the Centre – the North Atlantic. Here, the task involves what is – and always has been – the Navy's traditional role: the defence of merchant shipping.

In peacetime the Royal Navy is involved at levels ranging from perhaps only one ship to a dozen or more in a variety of exercises notably in the Western and South-Western Approaches. Because of the constant rotation of ships East of Suez and elsewhere and the needs to give ships' companies leave, not to mention the considerable amount of maintenance required in modern warships, it is impossible to say how many of the Royal Navy's ships at any given moment would be immediately available to NATO.

But, as has been mentioned earlier, every British warship with the exception of the five patrol vessels in Hong Kong, is earmarked for NATO in emergency. The 11 Royal Naval Reserve coastal minesweepers are in fact directly allocated to NATO and would at once form a NATO MCM squadron wherever the Supreme Allied Commander Atlantic (SACLANT) required them. The targeting for the computers in the four British Polaris submarines has also been agreed with NATO – a somewhat academic exercise by Mr Harold Wilson's Labour Government which permitted him to claim that his Party was not maintaining 'independent' British nuclear weapons.

Apart from frequent exercises particularly in the field of antisubmarine warfare and mine countermeasures, the Royal Navy contributes to NATO in a variety of ways, many of which remain virtually unknown outside the Service.

For some years now the Portland 'work-up' base has been training four Dutch and four West German destroyer/frigate type ships every year. The intensive seven-week 'work-up' involves exercises with submarines, aircraft, helicopters, fast target boats simulating missile boats, auxiliaries and other warships. The crews are also trained to handle a variety of problems ashore from fire-fighting to disaster relief which may involve anything

HMS *Norfolk* (centre) exercising with STANAVFORLANT in the Baltic Approaches in October 1972. The vessels are from left to right: HMNorS *Stavanger*, USS *Bigelow*, HMS *Norfolk*, HMNS *Amsterdam* and HMNorS *Oslo./Courtesy Commodore Fieldhouse*

from rescuing 'victims' from shattered buildings to controlling 'mobs'.

At Culdrose, Cornwall, naval air station crews for Norwegian Air Force Sea King helicopters have recently been replaced in the training cycle by West Germans. This will culminate in the somewhat unusual occasion when the first German naval Sea King squadron is formally commissioned in Britain.

Dutch submarine crews, for example, undergo escape training in the 100ft training tower in HMS *Dolphin*, the Gosport, Hants, Submarine Branch headquarters. Two Dutch submarines are now permanently based at the Clyde submarine base at Faslane, each submarine spending 14 weeks operating from Faslane before being relieved by another from Holland.

Many NATO naval officers undergo a variety of training in Royal Navy establishments ranging from staff courses at the Royal Naval College, Greenwich, to instruction at the Aircraft Direction School at Yeovilton, Somerset, naval air station. At places like Northwood, headquarters of the British Commander-in-Chief Fleet who is also NATO Commander-in-Chief Channel and Eastern Atlantic, many staff jobs are held by officers

from other NATO navies and the Admiral's NATO deputy is a Dutch Flag Officer.

One particularly vital and little known task the Royal Navy performs for merchant ships of the NATO nations, and indeed for ships from many other countries, is the running of the NCS – Naval Control of Shipping organisation. The NCS officers, drawn from the RNR, in emergency would be responsible in commercial ports for seeing that merchant ship masters received their convoy routing instructions; were aware of hazards like minefields and wrecks; that they observed regulations regarding lights; movements and so on.

Assisting with this important task is the Royal Naval Auxiliary Service. There is an RNXS unit in most major commercial ports and each unit usually has its own inshore minesweeper or Fleet tender to serve as a despatch vessel and to ferry NCS staff to ships in ports and anchorages and so on. RNXS personnel are civilians of both sexes and though many formerly served at sea others are completely of amateur status.

At the various NATO naval headquarters, notably Northwood, Fort Southwick, Pitreavie and Mount Batten, for exercises and in emergency many of the staff would be drawn from the Royal Naval (Headquarters) Reserve. These reservists, again of both sexes, are often naval pensioners or else young people with no naval experience.

Apart from the obvious shore support the Royal Navy provides for NATO with the various Maritime Headquarters, there are several other establishments in various parts of the British Isles which serve the Alliance. At Pembroke Dock, formerly (until 1926) Pembroke Royal Dockyard, in Wales, is a huge marine salvage and boom defence depot. Here are based a number of salvage, boom defence and diving craft but a considerably larger number of such vessels is moored at Pembroke for use by NATO in emergency.

In Scotland there is a NATO oil storage depot near the Clyde approaches while at Aultbea there is a boom defence and oil storage depot on a care and maintenance basis. Certain West German naval equipment is stored in the north of England while at Londonderry and Thurso the American Navy has radio stations although these, like the anchorage in the Holy Loch for an American submarine depot ship and the eight-ship POLARIS missile submarine squadron she supports, are there under a bilateral rather than NATO agreement.

These often obscure establishments are increasingly playing their part in supporting the NATO navies as one of the purposes of the STANAVFORLANT is to test the logistic support that various NATO countries can provide. It would be little use in a crisis having a multi-national squadron whose individual ships had to return to their own dockyards every time they needed a minor spare or to carry out routine maintenance.

In time of peace, inevitably, the NATO navies spend much of their time on routine exercises which attract no public attention unless something goes badly wrong. Certainly, there are times when the tables are turned and NATO warships shadow Russian ships on exercises.

But for the most part the NATO navies, and the Royal Navy is no exception, perform their tasks 'out of sight and out of mind'. It is not being chauvinistic to say that the Royal Navy plays its part fully in the Alliance, perhaps more fully than some other nations' navies, but when deficiencies and shortcomings do arise the fault ultimately lies with the politicians and those who voted them into office. Perhaps it is always impossible in peacetime to convince the people in a democracy that, like the individual, the country must have 'life insurance' and that adequate 'cover' cannot be obtained if the premiums are constantly being reduced.

Yet there can be no escaping the fact that the NATO navies are being increasingly overstretched as the Soviet Navy goes from strength to strength around the world. And as Soviet seapower grows greater so does the risk of a conflict, perhaps by miscalculation. The Soviet policy today is a gradual one of 'nudging' the West off the oceans. The time may not be far distant when either a stand must be made or the West will have to climb down and surrender control of the seas upon which its unity and therefore strength depend.

# The German Federal Navy

VICE-ADMIRAL F. RUGE

With the end of World War II in the spring of 1945 the German Armed Forces disappeared almost completely. Officers and men went into captivity or back to civil life, organisation and infrastructure were abolished, and all means of arms production was dismantled. Only some logistic units were transformed into semi-military Labour units, and most of the minesweeping squadrons kept in service to clear shipping channels under Allied supervision.

However, in a zone of political tension such as Central Europe a military vacuum will not exist for any length of time. As early as 1946 the Soviets, in the part of Germany occupied by them, set up purely German military forces camouflaged as 'People's Police in Barracks'. By 1950, this 'police' had a strength of 100,000 men, formed into two army corps and a small coastal navy. At that time the military weakness of the western Allies in Europe could not be disregarded any more. The Brussels Pact (1948) and the creation of NATO (1949) were followed by negotiations with the newly formed (1949) Federal Republic of Germany about a participation in the defence. Chancellor Adenauer convened a conference of 15 former officers (among them three ex-Navy) to give their opinions on the size and form of such a contribution.

## The Plans

Right from the beginning the naval experts acknowledged the paramount importance of a strong army and a tactical air force for making the Central-European front safe

*Gorch Fock* sail training ship of the German Federal Navy./*German Navy Official*

against any attempt of eastern aggression, but they also pointed out the importance of the Danish Narrows as the No 1 strategic position in North-Western Europe. As a consequence they saw the following military tasks for a German naval contribution:

- First and foremost assisting in the defence of the Danish position together with the Danish armed forces and German land and air units.
- Secondly hampering Soviet operations and supply traffic in the Baltic.
- Thirdly safeguarding NATO supply traffic through the North Sea.

Presupposing that some Allied destroyers would take part in these tasks the following naval strength was considered as a minimum requirement:

- 12 torpedoboats of 1,200 tons (also fast minelayers)
- 36 fast patrol boats (FPBs) with torpedoes and for minelaying

- 24 submarines of 250 tons, specially designed for use in the Baltic
- 12 escort vessels of 800 tons
- 24 minesweepers of 600 tons
- 36 small fast minesweepers of 100 tons
- 12 submarine chasers
- 36 guard cutters
- 36 small landing craft (12 with short-range rockets)
- 30 reconnaissance planes
- 30 planes for bombing and submarine hunting
- 84 fighters; small assault craft

In view of the experience of several navies in the last war particular stress was laid on a small naval air arm.

During the negotiations for admittance to the European Defence Community (EDC) this list was reduced to a minesweeping force with some FPBs. After EDC foundered in 1954, the Federal Republic was quickly made a member of NATO, very much through the efforts of Prime Minister Eden. At the same time it joined the Western European Union (WEU), the successor of the Brussels Pact. The strength of the 'Bundesmarine' (Federal Navy) was fixed at:

- 12 destroyers
- 2 minelayers
- 12 submarines
- 40 fast patrol boats
- 24 coastal minesweepers
- 30 small fast minesweepers
- 6 escort vessels
- 12 landing craft
- 10 guard vessels
- 58 fighter-bombers
- 20 anti-submarine aircraft.

The size of the surface ships was limited to 3,000 tons and that of the submarines to 350 tons. This also applied to ships of the fleet train and vessels used for training purposes. The WEU had to watch over the observance of these limitations, but Germany could apply for changes which seemed necessary and were approved by NATO. In this way, in 1960, the number of the submarines was increased to 24 (as in the first plans), their size to

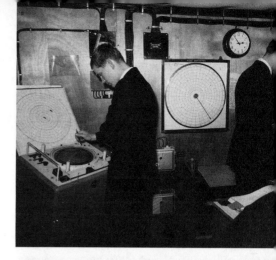

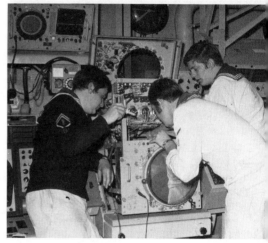

*Top:* Cadets under tactical training at Wilhelmshaven./*German Navy Official*

*Above:* Maintenance duties on board a warship./*German Navy Official*

450 tons, and that of 20 surface vessels (including 8 destroyers) to 6,000 tons. In addition, at the request of NATO, construction of 6 submarines of 750 tons for anti-submarine warfare was permitted.

### The beginning

The first few members of the new 'Bundeswehr' (Federal Armed Forces) took their oath on November 2nd, 1955, and the actual build-up began in January 1956, decidedly a part of the Alliance, not as an independent force as in a long and eventful past. Therefore the Navy, particularly in the first years, laid far more stress on training its men for effective cooperation with the allied navies, than on the most modern material and the newest technical developments. It was much better to get obsolete but reliable British frigates quickly than to wait several years for new destroyers and then to need more time to get them into working order. It was more important to start with officers and ratings who could speak English and French, than with specialists for the newest electronic equipment.

Of course, the technical aspects were not at all neglected, but after the complete interruption of ten years it was not easy to catch up with the latest developments. The estimate that for each of those years another year of reconstruction would be needed proved approximately correct. Without the help of the allied navies it would have taken much longer. The Royal Navy gave very valuable assistance, especially in the field of naval aviation. It lent a team of first-class advisers under Captain E. Brown, RN, and trained the first German squadrons (of Seahawks and Gannets) at Lossiemouth and Eglinton.

Six FPBs, built after the war for the British occupation authorities and manned by German personnel, were handed over in 1956 and formed a welcome nucleus of the FPB-flotilla.

Every German sailor who was sent abroad for any kind of training first received instruction in the language in question. Of about 3,000 men who in the first five years went to Allied navies (mostly to Britain and America) only about half a dozen had to return because they had difficulties with the language.

### The Organisation

The new navy was organised very simply. Department VII (Navy) was one of the 12 departments of the Ministry of Defence. Under it there were:

● Fleet Command (in all matters besides operations)
● Training
● Logistics (called 'Fleet Base')

In the sixties, Fleet Base was merged with Fleet Command. As was to be expected this proved too much for the staff of the Fleet. On October 1st, 1972, Fleet Base was reinstituted.

In the meantime 'Training' changed its name to 'Marine-Amt', ie 'General Naval Office', which is responsible for training, armament, and the naval medical service. Consequently, it is in command of all training ships and establishments, as well as of all installations for developing and testing ships and weapons. Of course, training and education are as vitally important as ever.

On paper the organisation of the Ministry of Defence looked simple too, but in reality it was not. It had seven civilian departments (administration, budget, personnel, housing, law, supply, technics) and five military departments (armed forces, army, air force, navy, medical services). All departments were directly under the Minister of Defence and his right hand, a state secretary (civil servant or politician), and independent of each other. On the military side the senior officer ('General-Inspekteur' with the rank of Four-Star-General) had the right to give directives in general military matters to the senior officers of the three Services ('Inspekteure' of army, air force and navy, with the rank of Three-Star-General). These four officers were (and still are) entirely responsible for building up and training their services, but their rights were minimal. In all matters concerning the civil departments (eg personnel or armament) they could make suggestions only. If the Inspector of the Navy could not reach an agreement with the head of the technical department eg on the question of whether a floating dock should get some kind of propulsion or not, only the Minister of Defence or his State Secretary could give a decision. The same procedure had to be followed in all matters of personnel and procurement. It is not surprising, therefore, that quite a number of problems were shelved because under this system it took too much time to solve them.

In the last few years this organisation has been improved, especially in the development of weapons and the construction of ships. There are now 'system controllers' ('System-Beauftragte'). ie officers co-ordinating military requirements and technical development of weapons systems.

## Personnel

The initial increase of the Navy personnel is shown in the diagram below. From 1961 on it continued to grow slowly until it reached 36,000 in 1969. This figure has not changed.

Right from the start it proved impossible to find sufficient volunteers for the careers of officer and petty officer. Enough qualified former officers rejoined to fill most of the important positions and in the first years this was a great help. The consequences of the gap of ten years are best shown by diagram, too. (See diagram opposite).

To increase the number of young officers the institution of 'temporary officer' was created. These men sign on for at least four and up to 12 years, on leaving they receive a corresponding bonus. This scheme has improved the situation and gives the Navy a considerable number of reserve officers. The plan to arrange the training of all the officers of the Bundeswehr in such a way that they receive a certificate, acknowledged in civil life as a university degree, has already attracted more aspirants. It will operate from 1973 on. Actually the training of the naval officers was so intensive from the start that the new scheme will not take much more time. Originally training began with three months each of military, technical and seamanship fundamentals (the latter carried out in a sailing ship), followed by a voyage of nine months in a power-driven training ship. Then came a year at the Naval Academy and a further year for weapons, machinery, tactics, and communications.

## Sail training

Sail training in the three-masted bark *Gorch Fock* of 1,600 tons was reintroduced not for purely romantic reasons, as is sometimes alleged, but for very practical purposes. Only this type of ship can quickly give the feeling for wind, weather and sea particularly necessary in a navy composed of small ships. Here the weather is far more interesting for the cadets than in a well-heated class-room of the Naval Academy. Therefore the meteorologist and his science were transferred to the *Gorch Fock*. Moreover, she is the only ship

Table 1. Development of Naval personnel, January 1956—January 1961.

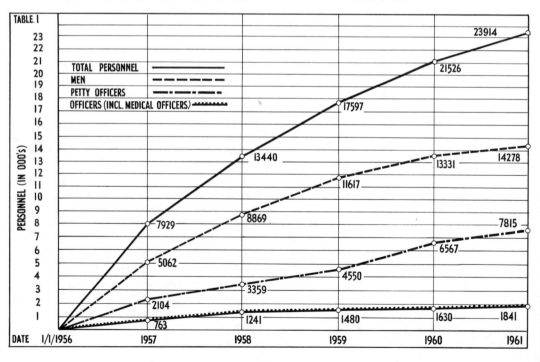

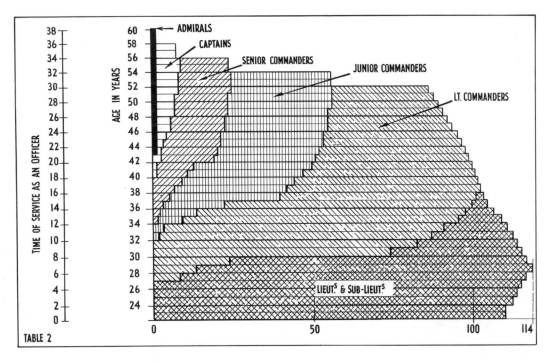

Table 2. Pyramid of ranks of Naval Officers
(theory), June 10, 1961.

Table 3. Pyramid of ranks of Naval Officers
(reality), August 1.

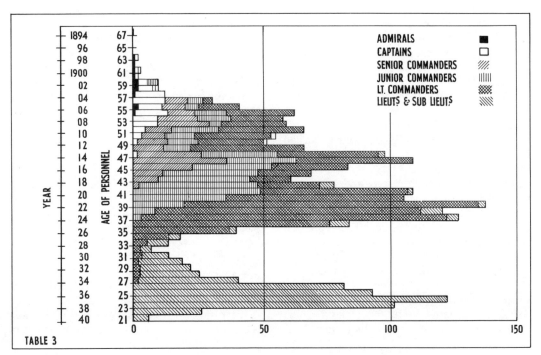

where the entire crew work together for one aim literally under the eyes of the captain. Then going aloft is a challenge which will help to bring out the personalities. Finally, this ship is a kind of psychological icebreaker, which was much needed in the first years of rebuilding the Navy but is still valuable in this respect.

Under the new scheme cadets live on board the sail training ship during their two months of basic military training and then go to sea in her for another two months. After a total of 15 months of basic instruction (including the trip in a power driven training ship) they attend an Armed Forces University for three years (each of three terms of three months, two months of special military instruction and one month leave). During this time they begin to some extent to specialise. It remains to be seen how far it will be possible to follow general university curricula and yet receive enough professional naval training.

All aspirants for naval career officer receive the same basic training which is to give them an insight into the essentials of their profession and to facilitate the choice of their specialisation. This is not rigid, as formerly, when once an engineer officer meant always an engineer officer. There are no fixed branches, changes are possible, and the road to leading positions is open to everyone. Here, character, leadership and knowledge should be weighed.

Selected Lieutenant-Commanders attend the Armed Forces Academy, together with Army and Air Force Captains. There are special positions in the higher staffs earmarked for those who have successfully passed through this training. The Army and Air Force permit the holders to add 'i.G.' (im Generalstab, ie 'in the general staff') to their military rank. The Navy has declined to do so because this seems to be a preferment which is not in the general interests of the service.

It is intended that one more step shall be added in the form of a Defence Academy for Colonels and naval Captains (and civil servants of similar rank) as preparation for commanding large units from the brigade upwards, and for corresponding staff positions. In the spring of 1971 a special board of

the Ministry of Defence finished a thorough examination of training and education in the Armed Forces and worked out a detailed plan which has now been put into execution. The Navy was already working along similar lines which it had followed from the beginning and which unofficially it called 'studium generale navale'.

With Petty Officers and ratings the situation is somewhat better because vacancies can be filled with conscripts. At first the Navy had expected to have no more than 10 per cent conscripts, but now it is almost 30 per cent. In 1971 the time for military service was reduced from 18 to 15 months, which made things still more difficult. On the other hand many of the conscripts take a liking to naval life and stay on. They receive an excellent training in their special fields. In addition every man who is selected for Petty Officer is prepared for his new position in a special 'Petty Officers' School'. There he is taught basic pedagogic and psychological requirements before he is promoted.

Those who volunteer for four years or more receive vocational training and preparation for civilian life partly during their active service, partly immediately afterwards, up to six months after four to six years of service, and up to 36 months after serving more than 12 years. There are over a hundred different possibilities, *eg* welder or engineer, interpreter or civil servant. They can also prepare themselves for business or examinations admitting them to higher technical schools or even universities.

## THE MATERIAL
### Old ships

In order to build up quickly, as demanded by the German Government, it was imperative to start practical training at sea as soon as possible. Officers and Petty Officers who had been in the former Navy had not only to relearn much but also to unlearn *eg* signals and tactical expressions. Instead they had to accustom themselves to NATO tactics and signals and to give their orders and reports in English or French. It was fortunate that the 'Bundesgrenzschutz' (federal frontier police), formed from 1951 on, had set up a

*Top:* Destroyer *Hamburg*, one of four similar vessels completed during the mid-60's./*German Navy Official*

*Above:* The latest class destroyer to enter service with the German Federal Navy is an American type 'Charles F. Adams' class. Three of these vessels have been built in the United States for Germany and the design modified to meet German requirements. The vessel shown here is the *Lutjens.*/*German Navy Official*

*Above:* The first submarines designed and built by Germany after World War II were the 11 coastal craft of the Type 205. *U9* is shown here./*German Navy Official*

*Below:* The latest submarine type *U13.*/*German Navy Official*

*Foot:* Type 148 fast patrol boat. Note the launchers for EXOCET missiles aft of the bridge./*German Navy Official*

small naval branch under former naval officers. Most of its 30 guard and patrol vessels were small, 60 to 140 tons, but two ex-Canadian corvettes of 480/750 tons were well suited to serve as the first training ships for cadets and petty officers.

Farsighted American naval officers had kept a minesweeping Labour Service unit alive. This yielded six large minesweepers (600 tons, coal-burning), 12 fast minesweepers), (R-type of 140 tons) and a number of guard boats. Together with the six British FPBs already mentioned and five large oil-burning minesweepers given back by the French Navy these mini-fleets made it possible to begin training quickly. As early as spring 1957 two minesweeping squadrons took part in NATO manoeuvres.

Seven frigates ('Black Swan' and 'Hunt' class) were cheaply bought from the British Government, and America lent six 'Fletcher'-class destroyers. All these vessels were ready for service in 1958/9 and proved invaluable. Two very small submarines (250 tons of the German Type XXIII, scuttled at the end of the war and later refloated, were found to be in surprisingly good condition and were put into service within a short time. A large submarine, Type XXI (1620/1820 tons), was raised later. With reduced engine power, without armament and manned with a civilian crew she is still used for underwater tests and experiments.

## New construction

Designs for most of the smaller craft were prepared during the EDC negotiations, and orders could be placed when Germany joined NATO. Of the 24 coastal minesweepers six were built by the Amiot Shipyard at Cherbourg to the plans of the French 'Mercure' class (333/380 tons, 15 knots). They came according to plan and proved very seaworthy and handy. The other 18, slightly larger and faster (370/420 tons, 16.5 knots) resembled the United States 'Bluebird' class, but were glued wood throughout, not a single piece of metal being used in frames or hull. The diesel engines were, as far as was possible, made of amagnetic material. The magnetic field of these ships was extremely weak, and

the glue proved tougher than the wood it kept together, but their stability was too low and their quarter-deck cramped. So the uppermost part of the bridge was cut off and 14 feet glued on aft. This gave more room for handling minesweeping gear and improved the handling in a seaway.

For the fast minesweepers of the 'R' class (230/280 tons) the Voith-Schneider drive was selected, instead of propellers. Two horizontal rotating discs under the stern with vertical moveable 'knives' give an unsurpassed manoeuvrability (turning *on the spot* 360° will take no more than seven seconds). This arrangement had been used to great advantage before and during the war in more than 100 R-boats and a few large minesweepers. The new R-boat was designed for 24 knots, however, as against the 17 knots achieved previously, and there had been no time for practical tests. Now it was found that no more than about 18 could be reached, and the boats had to be equipped with variable-pitch propellers. This necessitated considerable changes in the first four vessels and delayed completion of the others. They were commissioned from 1958 on.

Building 40 fast patrol boats of 160/190 tons with a speed of 42 knots did not offer any particular difficulties because the Lürssen Shipyard at Vegesack, near Bremen, had already built the six for the British. But not everything went smoothly with this new class. The output of their diesels (four in each vessel) was increased from 2,500hp to 3,000hp, and a long time elapsed before they were entirely satisfactory. The FPBs were commissioned between 1957 and 1963. The initial engine trouble made longer overhauls necessary but did not prevent them from taking part in exercises. Six weeks every spring together with Danish and Norwegian FPBs were particularly rewarding. In addition 21 days of annual NATO exercises were held, seven days each of which was spent in Danish, Norwegian and German waters, under corresponding command, and with the weekends in ports there. This kind of working together is a practical way to improve relations between the allied navies and to strengthen the Alliance.

Orders for the six frigates of the 'Köln' class (2,090/2,500 tons armed with two 100mm and six 40mm guns as well as ample ASW weapons) were placed with the Stülcken Yard at Hamburg which had formerly built minesweepers and small escort vessels. They were completed between 1961 and 1964. They have four diesels of 3,000hp for cruising at 18 knots, and two gas turbines of 12,000hp. Two motors and one turbine are geared to one shaft with a variable pitch propeller. This arrangement has worked very well, top speed being 32 knots.

Of the 12 destroyers of the programme, Parliament granted funds only for four because in the eyes of some experts the need for these comparatively large vessels was questionable. Actually they are maids of all work, and the best minelayers under the special conditions of the Danish position. It took 17 months alone to place the orders because most shipyards did not feel equal to the task. Finally Stülcken accepted, but building the vessels took much longer than predicted. The last was commissioned in 1968. Their characteristics are: 3,000/4,000 tons, four 100mm and eight 40mm guns, five torpedo tubes, ASW armament, four boilers, two turbines, 68,000hp, 35 knots.

### Guns and missiles

The calibre of 100mm is somewhat light but the gun (French) can fire 70 rounds per minute, and it was the only single mount available at that time. It was planned later on to exchange the two guns aft for Ship-to-air missiles. In 1957 it was too early for this step, but the problem was examined. The Technical Department was of the opinion that the best way would be to 'navalise' the HAWK missile. Nothing came of this idea for ten years.

In the meantime the necessity for missiles in combat vessels had become much clearer, and other navies had made much progress. In order not to lose touch completely the Government in 1964 allowed the purchase of three destroyers of the American 'Charles F. Adams' class with TARTAR missiles. Their keels were laid at the Bath Iron Works in Maine in 1966 and 1967, and they were ready for service three years later. They

displace 3,370/4,500 tons and are armed with two 127mm guns, one TARTAR launcher and ASW weapons. Their speed is 35 knots, and they have proved extremely satisfactory. The idea of rearming the four destroyers of the 'Hamburg' class was abandoned.

The largest ship of the Bundesmarine is the training ship *Deutschland* of 4,880/5,400 tons, armed with four 100mm and six 40mm guns and all kinds of ASW weapons. She has diesels and turbines, and her top speed is 21 knots.

### Submarines

Submarine construction has met with severe setbacks. No allied navy had built boats as small as 350 tons, and the first keels could not be laid before 1961 (at Emden). The design is excellent, with eight torpedo tubes and an under-water speed of 17 knots (in short bursts). On trials they did all that was expected from them, but the amagnetic steel of the hulls corroded quickly. Remedies like insulating paint or zinc plates were tried, but the only adequate solution were new hulls of a thoroughly tested steel. This cost much money and time, and the second 12 vessels were delayed. *U 13* was commissioned in 1972, and the remaining eleven boats will soon follow.

Norway was loaned *U 3* for trying out this type, and then ordered 15 similar boats to be built of normal steel. They were completed between 1964 and 1967.

The five ASW submarines of 750 tons, authorised by WEU, are still in the planning stage.

### Naval air

The 'Naval Air Division' is fully integrated in the Fleet. The aircraft chosen were British Seahawks and Gannets because they were a thoroughly tried design and entirely dependable. When they wore out they were replaced by the F 104 (Starfighter) and the Bréguet 1150 Atlantic. The Starfighter was selected in close contact with the German Air Force, which had decided on this aircraft after long deliberation. Having the same type made logistics and basic training more economic. The Starfighter met the Navy's requirements for armed reconnaissance, and losses were no higher than with the Seahawks. On the whole, a two-seater would have been preferable, and the plans for the next generation of planes aim in this direction.

For search and rescue there are helicopters (among them Sycamores), for transport and communications British Pembrokes. From 1973 onwards Sea Kings will replace the older helicopters.

## The role of the Merchant Marine

Although in naval policy the Merchant Marine plays an important part, the Navy's relations with it have not always been good. Therefore the Bundesmarine has made special efforts to improve relations. The subdepartment of the Navy Staff dealing with all matters of sea transport was transferred to Hamburg into the Department of Shipping of the Ministry of Transport and Traffic. Co-operation was greatly facilitated by reserve officers who joined the Bundesmarine, and by naval officers who after the war had served on merchant ships.

It was soon agreed that members of the Merchant Marine would not be called up to serve in the Navy, but would receive special training in their duties aboard their merchant ships in an emergency, eg damage control, NATO signalling, convoy tactics, procedure in case of submarine or air attack, etc. The aim is to have the ships competently handled within the organisation set up by the Planning Board of Ocean Shipping of NATO. This will give them the best chances to reach their ports of destination in the case of a conflict.

A Sea King rescue helicopter./*German Navy Official*

## The composition of the Fleet

At the end of 1972 the following combat forces were assigned to NATO:

- 3 destroyer squadrons with 11 destroyers
- 1 escort squadron with 6 frigates
- 4 fast patrol boat squadrons with 38 FPBs
- 1 submarine squadron with 6 submarines + 5 training
- 2 naval air wings with 120 Starfighters
- 1 naval air wing with 20 Atlantics

In addition there were the following combat support units:

- 6 minesweeping squadrons (5 assigned) with 55 vessels
- 2 minelayers
- 1 landing squadron with 12 landing craft
- 1 fleet train and utility squadron (5 sub-chasers)

To support this fleet there were:

- 11 tenders (for submarines, FPBs and minesweepers)
- 10 store or ammunition ships
- 10 tankers
- 20 liaison aircraft
- 20 sea and rescue helicopters.

C-in-C Fleet (a three-star admiral) with the assigned forces comes directly under the NATO Naval Commander of the Baltic Approaches (ComNavBaltAp). He is in charge of all Baltic operations, with a two-star Admiral under him detailed to command the forces operating in the North Sea.

## Present Problems and Developments

As far as can be seen there will not be any important change in the organisation and tasks of the Fleet. Some of the ships may temporarily be attached to NATO groups such as STANAVFORLANT (Standing Naval Force Atlantic) or form a similar task force for home waters.

Wear and tear and technical development will make it necessary to replace the older ships. Most of those which formed the first squadrons have already been scrapped, and the American loan destroyers are about to follow. For their replacement the special conditions in the Baltic and North Sea have to be kept in mind and also the defence budget of the Federal Republic.

In the middle of the sixties there were plans for corvettes with missiles and a tactical data processing system for a combat group. However, whilst on the drawing board they grew to such a size and correspondingly increased cost that they were never built. A newer and more practical development is the construction of a new type of FPB. The '148' class was developed in close collaboration with the French. *S 41*, the first of 20 boats of this type, was launched at Cherbourg at the end of September 1972. The boats displace 250 tons, have a speed of 42 knots, and are armed with a 76mm and 40mm gun, wire-controlled torpedoes and ship-to-ship missiles of the French type EXOCET (range 38 kilometers). Ten of the '143' class, somewhat larger and armed with dual-purpose missiles, are under construction.

Altogether a medium-sized navy has come into existence, manned and equipped in such a way that it should be able to accomplish its tasks in the Alliance. The continuous growth of the Soviet Navy makes it quite evident to every sailor that there is no détente on the oceans. More than ever the life of the nations in Western Europe depends on unrestricted sea communications. They have to cooperate closely with the other side of the North Atlantic to keep the sea and themselves free. This basic situation would not change if ever the European Economic Community should be united politically and form its own defence forces. This would further facilitate military co-operation and standardisation, with much saving of money. But contact with North America would be as vital as before. It is a purely continental and limited view to see the North Atlantic as a dividing obstacle. Actually, the peoples on both sides of the Atlantic are much closer to each other than Western Europe is to Russia. Not even inside the Soviet Empire is there anything like the free flow of men and ideas across the Atlantic in both directions.

In the foreseeable future, therefore, a West-European defence force will never be able to fill the place of NATO. The Bundesmarine is fully aware of this and of the fact, that as a part of the Armed Forces, it is a means of politics. Military strategy is only a part of Grand Strategy for which the statesman at the head of the Government is responsible with the aim of preserving or re-establishing peace.

Therefore as recently as October 1st, 1972, the Bundesmarine formulated its missions as follows:

- to contribute, by its presence, readiness and conduct at sea to the deterrent power of the Alliance and to its strenthening, and the maintenance of order at sea;
- to work for the prestige of the Federal Republic of Germany and to further her international relations;
- to look after national rights and to safeguard national interests at sea, and on the German part of the continental shelf;
- to serve the Government as an instrument of flexible crisis management by its presence and conduct at sea;
- to protect, in a defence emergency, the territories of coastal NATO countries and the Baltic approaches by countering attacks directed against the Baltic and North Sea coasts. It is the Navy's mission to restrict, to the degree ensuring that protection, the enemy's use of the Baltic, to deny the enemy his lines of communication between naval bases in the Baltic and in the Atlantic, and to guarantee, in co-operation with our Allies, control of the North Sea.

These missions are based on NATO defence agreements and were defined in consultation with members of the Alliance.

To the Bundesmarine they are the guide lines for training its men and improving its material. As in the 18 years since its inception it will continue to co-operate as closely as possible with the allied navies. It is convinced that in view of the growth of Soviet sea power NATO has to be kept alive and strong if the free Atlantic world is to survive.

# Twenty Years of American Naval Guided Missiles

## S. TERZIBASCHITSCH*

The end of World War II brought the first effective attempts to replace the piston engined aircraft with the newly developed jet engined plane, which promised to be much faster, have a quicker rate of climb and a much higher ceiling. The development of the jet enabled the American Navy to deploy its first jet aircraft in the Korean War. By this time it had become clear that the use of jet aircraft by large navies would cause a revolution in many branches of defence technology. However, the fact that the jet aircraft was much faster than its pistoned counterpart was not the sole reason for the new conception of air defence in the American Navy. The end of World War II also brought the realisation that a missile could be as effective when used against sea and air targets, as against land targets, and in addition could be operated by aircraft and ships as well as by land troops. The creation of the nuclear warhead as an effective offensive weapon brought for the Navy many problems, especially when it became clear the the Soviet Union was also in a position to deliver atomic bombs. The American Navy was now confronted with the fact that the jet aircraft, guided missiles and nuclear warheads would in future pose a considerable threat to its operational credibility. It became clear that the naval weapons then available would be ineffective against fast, high flying enemy aircraft and missiles. It was now essential that all enemy aircraft should be intercepted and destroyed well outside the range of any possible Air-to-ship

* For further illustrations applicable to this article please see following article on Surface-to-Air missiles.

missile which they might carry, and certainly before they were in any position to launch such a missile. This, then, was the moment to create an entirely new concept in air defence. Only the guided missile would be capable of meeting such a challenge. This meant the development of a completely new technology, and the American Navy had to create an entire surface fleet of new ships suitable for carrying such missiles. The realisation of this enormous task has taken about 17 years, commencing about 1952 with the intention to introduce Surface-to-air missiles, and ending about 1969, when all the newly constructed or converted ships had joined the fleet. However, construction of guided missile ships proceeds; but in future all new construction will be replacing older units, which in the meantime have been decommissioned, or utilising newer and more sophisticated missile systems.

The history of the enormous build up of the American missile surface fleet is, of course, mainly a history of the air defence technology of the past twenty years. The motto of some 10 years of guided missile ship construction was: "missiles, only missiles, are the adequate solution". It was indeed unique and strange that the newly designed ships mounting powerful defence systems against supersonic, high-flying aircraft were unable to withstand the attack of small fast torpedo boats, or old, very low flying aircraft. The late President John F. Kennedy, himself a former navy man, was one of the first to recognize the danger of following this policy, and he gave the order that each guided missile ship must carry some guns to meet the requirement for a limited self-defence against such targets. How correct was this decision can be seen in retrospect following the *Pueblo* incident, where the probable presence of only a single 3in gun would have completely reversed the situation. In addition the experiences of the Vietnam War have also shown the need for effective gunnery systems for shore bombardment in support of the army.

The first officially announced operational missile launch by the Navy was achieved in 1948, when the converted fleet submarine

*Above:* Guided missile cruiser *Long Beach*. Note the unique fixed radar surfaces on the sides of the bridge structure, and the long reloading magazine in front of the bridge./*A. J. Watts Collection*

*Left:* This view of the USS *Albany* shows the TALOS launcher forward and the starboard TARTAR launcher. SPG 49 and SPW 2 control gear are placed on the magazine. The forward 'Mack' bears the SPS 48, the aft the SPS 43 radar aerial. The SPS 30 is visible on the aft radar support. To the left of the *Albany* is the *William V. Pratt*, carrying an SPS 52 radar on the forward mast and an SPS 37 aft./*S. Terzibaschitsch*

*Below: Galveston* prior to decommission. The *Topeka* carried a reverse arrangement of the SPS 30 and SPS 52 radar aerial on the mainmast and after deckhouse./*S. Terzibaschitsch*

*Cusk* launched the LOON guided missile. This was of course, a Surface-to-surface missile based on the former German V-1 flying bomb deployed at the end of World War II. Later, in 1957, the REGULUS I Surface-to-surface missile was introduced, having a range of 500 miles, and capable of being launched from submarines (*Tunny, Barbero, Growler, Grayback*), as well as from aircraft carriers (*Bon Homme Richard, Hancock, Randolph, Lexington, Shangri La, Bennington, Lake Champlain*) and heavy cruisers (*Los Angeles, Helena, Macon, Toledo*). The successor to the REGULUS I missile was the REGULUS II, with a range of about 1,000 miles. The nuclear driven submarine *Halibut* was especially designed for the utilisation of this missile, and the new cruiser *Long Beach* was also capable of launching this missile. The REGULUS of course was a Surface-to-surface missile designed for use against land targets. Later, in 1964–65 the development of the REGULUS series of missiles ceased in favour of the POLARIS ICBM (Intercontinental Ballistic Missile) system which was to be fitted in the SSBN submarines. The ships involved in the REGULUS programme have been partially reconverted to their former state, or used for other duties. Thus ended the development of the first of the American naval Surface-to-surface missile systems.

However, the development of Surface-to-air missiles was rapidly being forced on the American Navy. Three Surface-to-air shipborne missile systems were developed simultaneously:

TALOS (Bendix Corporation) with a range of 60+ miles for use on cruisers.
TERRIER I (General Dynamics) with a range of about 12 miles for use on cruisers and heavy frigates, and
TARTAR (General Dynamics) with a range of about 10 miles for use on destroyers and escorts.

Later all three systems were improved in range, but TALOS still retains the greater range, and in its latest development is suitable for use against surface as well as air targets. Some aircraft have been shot down during the Vietnam War using TALOS, but with the exception of the cruiser *Long Beach*, which has only one such system on board, all remaining cruisers fitted with TALOS are over age and will soon be decommissioned. The TERRIER I missle has been rapidly developed into the TERRIER II, the range being extended to about 20 miles. It is this missile which is now being fitted on all new frigates, and all the older frigates have also been modernised with this missile which uses a homing guidance system in place of the previous beam-riding system. At the start of the sixties a totally new Surface-to-air missile system was to have been developed, called TYPHON. There were to have been two versions of this missile – a close range (20 miles) and an extended range (about 200 miles). Lack of cost effectiveness, however, caused further development of the missile to be cancelled in 1964.

Unfortunately both the TERRIER and TARTAR have not proved as successful in operation as had been expected. In 1972 the General Accounting Office of the United States stated that the number of successful shoots was not very high compared with the number of missiles actually launched. It is not certain, however, whether this information was issued on the basis of intelligence requirements. Of course a number of difficulties have been encountered with the efficiency of these missile systems.

In the meantime a further new Surface-to-air system, the STANDARD, was developed, which began to enter service with the Fleet in the first half of the seventies. It utilises the same launchers, guidance and control equipment as the TERRIER and TARTAR, which missiles it will eventually replace. The STANDARD is being developed both as a medium range missile (range about 12 miles) and as an extended version (range about 30+ miles). There is also a Surface-to-surface version under development for use on small patrol boats or escorts as an anti-radiation missile. In this role, it can, if necessary, be fired from the existing ASROC launchers.

Apart from these complex systems, the Air-to-surface missile SPARROW III has been modified for close-range anti-air defence on those surface ships which are not armed with one of the above described systems. Its range is about 10+ miles. Ships carrying only this missile system are not officially classified as guided missile ships. Normally the missiles are stowed in a box-like launcher (up to eight in one launcher at a time), and are controlled by the Mk 76 control gear.

An entirely new missile system at present under development is the AEGIS (the former ASMS), intended to be fitted initially on the 'Virginia' class frigates in about the mid-seventies.

Since before about 1960 the first ships especially designed for the deployment of guided missiles joined the Fleet. Four single conversions of ships were used in the initial trials to gain knowledge of the efficiency of such a weapon system. In 1954 the old battleship *Mississippi*, until that time serving as a gunnery training ship (EAG 128), was fitted with two TERRIER I launchers aft for test purposes. Similar was the external arrangement of two TERRIER I launchers on the two converted heavy cruisers *Boston* (CAG 1) and *Canberra* (CAG 2), which were the first operational guided missile surface ships in the American Navy. The same year (1956) the destroyer *Gyatt* (DD 712) was recommissioned as DDG 1, to obtain experience with the TERRIER I system on board smaller ships. On the whole this proved fairly successful, but nevertheless the TERRIER launcher was somewhat too large a system for a destroyer, and only 14 missiles could be stowed in the magazine behind the launcher. Later, after it was decided to fit the lighter TARTAR missile on destroyers, the *Gyatt* lost her missile launcher and was again redesignated DD 712, serving as a trials ship for electronic equipment. Since that time it has been usual for destroyers and escorts to be armed with a TARTAR system, while the larger frigates and cruisers receive the TERRIER and TALOS systems respectively. All guided missile armed surface ships are considered as 'Anti-Air Warfare (AAW) vessels', and their main mission is to protect carrier task groups, as well as amphibious groups, replenishment groups, and the vital merchant ship convoys, against enemy aircraft. In addition, however, these ships also possess a considerable inventory of ASW weapons thus enabling them to act in a secondary role giving anti-submarine protection to the above mentioned groups. So, they are all true multi-purpose vessels.

The various main guided missile systems are always related to certain launchers, radar and missile control equipment, and the tables opposite gives a survey of all the surface guided missile ship classes of the American Navy, including the indication of such equipment.

In addition the following must be noted concerning the above mentioned classes:

*3 Attack Carriers: 'America'/'Kitty Hawk' class (CVA 63, 64, 66)*
These huge carriers are not classified as guided missile ships, although they possess two TERRIER II launchers aft. At present the SPS 52 radar is on the bridge. *Enterprise* (CVAN 65) was initially fitted to receive two TERRIER launchers aft, but was completed without any launchers, and served for a number of years without any weapon, with the exception of her own aircraft. Later she was armed with two BPDMS (Basic Point Defence Missile Systems) launchers using the SEA SPARROW close-defence missile. These have the associated SPS 32/33 radar system. The *John F. Kennedy* (CVA 67) was also originally intended to have two TARTAR systems aft, but for cost saving reasons this idea was abandoned, and three BPDMS launchers were installed, controlled with the Mk 76 Mod. 0 equipment. An SPS 48 antenna is fitted on this carrier, while the SPS 30, fitted in her near sister ships has been removed.

*1 Nuclear-powered guided missile cruiser: Long Beach (CGN 9)*
She was the first nuclear powered surface warship to be commissioned in the world. Three guided missile systems are embarked: two TERRIER II forward, one TALOS aft. SPS 32/33 radar is installed on the flanks of the conning tower. She was intended to carry REGULUS missiles, but instead an ASROC launcher for ASW was installed. For a while the installation of the POLARIS ICBM was contemplated, and space was reserved for the system, but later the idea was abandoned.

*3 Guided missile cruisers: 'Albany' class (CG10, 11, 12)*

Between 1958–64 these ships were totally converted from World War II heavy cruisers to the most powerful guided missile ships in the American Navy. Four missile systems are installed; one TALOS forward and one aft, and two TARTAR twin launchers abreast the bridge superstructure.

*2 Heavy cruisers (former guided missile cruisers): 'Boston' class (CA69, 70)*

The first American operational surface guided missile ships. Converted between 1952–56 as 'single-enders' with two TERRIER I twin launchers aft, one superimposed above the other. They only carried an experimental version of the modern 3-D radar. The missiles were originally controlled by updated fire control equipment, which was later replaced by the SPQ 5. The launchers can only be reloaded in the vertical position. Because the TERRIER I missile became obsolete both ships were reclassified as CA in 1968, and finished their role as gunfire support ships off Vietnam. They are now mothballed in Reserve Fleets.

*2 Guided missile light cruisers: 'Galveston' class (CLG 3, 8)*

Partly converted between 1956–60 from World War II light cruisers of the 'Cleveland' class. They retained two forward 6in gun turrets

| Type | Class | No. of Ships | Missile System* | Launcher | Control Gear | Associated Radar Systems† | Remarks |
|------|-------|-------------|-----------------|----------|--------------|---------------------------|---------|
| CVA | America/ Kitty Hawk | 3 | 2 Terrier II | 1 Mk 10 Mod. 3 1 Mk 10 Mod. 4 | 4 SPG 55 | SPS 52 (43, 30) | twin launcher |
| CGN | Long Beach | 1 | 1 Talos (40) + 2 Terrier II (140) | Mk 12 Mod. 0 Mk 10 Mod. 1 + 2 | 2 SPG 49 + 2 SPW 2; 4 SPG 55 | SPS 32 + 33 (12) | twin launcher |
| CG | Albany | 3 | 2 Talos (92) + 2 Tartar (80) | Mk 12 Mk 13 | 4 SPG 49 + 4 SPW 2; 4 SPG 51 | SPS 48 Albany SPS 52 others | SPS 43 in all 3, 1 SPS 30 in Albany 2 SPS 30 in others |
| CA | Boston | 2 | 2 Terrier I (144) | Mk 9 Mod. 1 | 2 SPQ 5 | experimental (43, 30) | twin launcher; ships in reserve fleets |
| CLG | Galveston Little Rock | 2 4 | 1 Talos (46) 1 Terrier I (120) | Mk 7 Mod. 0 Mk 9 Mod. 1 | 2 SPG 49 + 2 SPW 2; 2 SPQ 5 | SPS 52 (43, 30) Talos ships no 3-D-radar system | 1 Talos and 1 Terrier ship in reserve; twin launcher; SPS 30 instead of 3-D-radar |
| DLGN | Virginia | 3 | 2 Tartar later 2 Aegis | Mk 26; later ? | 4 SPG 51 later SPY 1 | SPS 48 (40) | dual twin launcher for Standard/ER + ASROC |
| DLGN | California | 2 | 2 Tartar | Mk 13 Mod. 3 | 4 SPG 51 Mk 76 | SPS 48 (40) | single launcher for Standard ER |
| DLGN | Truxtun | 1 | 1 Terrier II | Mk 10 Mod. 7 | 2 SPG 55 | SPS 48 (40) | dual twin launcher for Terrier/ASROC |
| DLGN | Bainbridge | 1 | 2 Terrier II (80) | Mk 10 | 4 SPG 55 | SPS 52 (37) | twin launcher; SPS 48 will be installed |
| DLG | Belknap | 9 | 1 Terrier II (40) | Mk 10 Mod. 7 | 2 SPG 55 | SPS 48 (40 or 37) | dual twin launcher for Terrier/ASROC |
| DLG | Leahy | 9 | 2 Terrier II (80) | Mk 10 Mod. 5 | 4 SPG 55 | SPS 48 (37) | twin launcher |
| DLG | Farragut | 10 | 1 Terrier II | Mk 10 Mod. 0 | 2 SPG 55 | SPS 48 (37) | twin launcher |
| DDG | Mitscher | 2 | 1 Tartar | Mk 13 Mod. 2 | 2 SPG 51 | SPS 48 (37) | single launcher |
| DDG | Charles F. Adams | 23 | 1 Tartar (40–42) | Mk 11 Mod. 0 Mk 13 Mod. 0 | 2 SPG 51 | SPS 52 (40 or 37) | first 13 ships have twin launcher and SPS 37, others single launcher and SPS 40 |
| DDG | Decatur | 4 | 1 Tartar | Mk 13 Mod. 1 | 1 SPG 51 | SPS 48 (40 or 37) | single launcher; only 1 ship has SPS 40 |
| DEG | Brooke | 6 | 1 Tartar (16) | Mk 22 | 1 SPG 51 | SPS 52 | light weight single launcher |

85 ships, 78 of which are in active service, 3 DLGN's in construction and 4 CA/CLG in Reserve Fleets.
\* Numbers in brackets refer to numbers of missiles carried
† First figure refers to associated 3-D-radar systems. Figures in parantheses refer to other main air surveillance systems.

and three 5in AA twin turrets. Both vessels lack flagship facilities. They are fitted with one missile system only: CLG 3 a TALOS and CLG 8 a TERRIER I aft, in single end arrangement. Before they decommissioned in 1969–70 both units had SPS 52 radar. They are now mothballed in Reserve Fleets.

*4 Guided missile light cruisers: 'Little Rock' class (CLG 4, 5, 6, 7)*
Converted in a similar fashion to CLG 3 between 1956–60, but retaining only one 6in and one 5in gun turret forward. In place of the second 6in turret they received an enlarged bridge with flag accommodation and extra space. CLG 4 and 5 received a TALOS missile system, and CLG 6 and 7 a TERRIER I system aft. These ships differed slightly in appearance to the CLG 3 class. A good aid to identification was that TALOS armed cruisers always had 3-D radars on the high lattice mast. At present the TERRIER armed ships still embark the SPS 52 radar, while the TALOS armed vessels had their SPS 39 radar removed some years ago and were not fitted with any replacement. Obviously the SPS 30 radar is now serving as a search radar for missile purposes as well as its other duties. The TERRIER armed ships still embark the SPQ 5 controls, and further modernisations are not anticipated in view of the age of the vessels. All four units are still serving as fleet flagships.

*3 Nuclear powered guided missile frigates: 'Virginia' class (DLGN 38, 39, 40)*
The first three units belonging to the former DXGN total package procurement programme. All under construction. At first they will be armed with two dual launchers, arranged in double end configuration. They can launch either the STANDARD ER or ASROC ASW torpedo. Later these ships are planned to be modified to carry the newly developed AEGIS system, again using two launchers as well as the fixed SPY 1 radar. It is probable that the SPS 48 radar will be retained.

*2 Nuclear powered guided missile frigates: 'California' class (DLGN 36, 37)*
The first flush-decked DLGN of the American

Navy. Similar to the 'Virginia' class, but with separate ASROC launcher and single purpose TARTAR D launchers forward and aft. It is possible that the AEGIS system will at a later date replace the TARTAR. The ships are almost completed. They are intended to serve primarily as nuclear escort for the *Nimitz* (CVAN 68), while the 'Virginia' class will act as escort for the *Dwight D. Eisenhower* (CVAN 69).

*1 Nuclear powered guided missile frigate: Truxtun (DLGN 35)*
The second DLGN of the American Navy, completed in 1967. One TERRIER dual launcher aft, destined for firing ASROC and TERRIER II missiles. The weapon arrangement corresponds with that of the 'Belknap' class, but in reversed configuration.

*1 Nuclear powered guided missile frigate: Bainbridge (DLGN 25)*
The first DLGN of the American Navy, completed in 1962. The missile arrangement is similar to the 'Leahy' class DLG; two TERRIER II launchers in double end configuration, and separate ASROC launcher. Advanced air warning capability will be updated following the completion of the 'Leahy' class modernisation about the beginning of 1973. Then SPS 48 radar and Mk 76 control equipment will be installed.

*9 Guided missile frigates: 'Belknap' class (DLG 26–34)*
The third generation of DLG's in the American navy. Single end missile ships with dual TERRIER II launcher forward as well as ASROC. Most sophisticated design; ships being completed between 1964 and 1967.

*9 Guided missile frigates: 'Leahy' class (DLG 16–24)*
The second generation of DLG's completed between 1962–64, and the first ones to have a 'Mack' instead of the usual funnels. Also the first vessels with a double end arrangement of TERRIER II launchers. All ships have received considerable modernisation, including Anti-Air Warfare (AAW) and ECM (electronic countermeasures) updating. This

USS *Leahy* showing appearance following **AAW** modernisation. Note the **SPS 48** radar antenna on the forward 'Mack' and the four **SPG 55** control modules./*Official US Navy*

modernisation included the installation of Mk 76 control equipment as well as SPS 48 radar. The standard of the weapons systems is now equal to that of the 'Belknap' class.

### 10 Guided missile frigates: 'Farragut' class (DLG 6–15)

The first generation of DLG's in the American Navy, all completed between 1960–61. Single ended vessels with one TERRIER II system aft. The four oldest vessels of this class originally had two SPQ 5 control equipment instead of SPG 55 installed in the later ships. Parallel with the 'Leahy' class all vessels of this class were modernised between 1969–72, receiving similar improvements such as NTDS, SPS 48 radar and Mk 76 control equipment. The standard of weapons is now equal to that of the 'Belknap' class.

All of the aforementioned frigate classes at present represent the most important AAW ships of the American Navy.

### ? Guided missile destroyers: DXG type

Initially it was planned to create a class of about 28 new DDG's belonging to the DXG procurement programme. In appearance they should be similar to the DD's of the 'Spruance' class (DD 963) with one gun replaced by the TARTAR D system. Because of the rising cost of development of the 'Spruance' class it is at the time of writing not

yet clear whether a part or whole of this proposed class will be built.

### 2 Guided missile destroyers: 'Mitscher' class (DDG 35, 36)

From 1966 to 1969 two former frigates were converted to DDG, receiving a single TARTAR launcher aft and SPS 48 radar. The conversion of two sister ships was not executed because of cost limitations.

### 8 Guided missile destroyers: 'Decatur' class (DDG 31–34)

Four former 'Forrest Sherman' class DD's were converted to DDG between 1965 and 1968. They received a single TARTAR launcher aft and SPS 48 radar. No further conversions in this series are planned.

### 23 Guided missile destroyers: 'Charles F. Adams' class (DDG 2–24)

The standard DDG type of the American Navy: all ships were completed between 1960 and 1964 as the first purpose built guided missile destroyer class. DDG 2–14 have a Mk 11 launcher aft, and DDG 15–24 a Mk 13 single launcher, which has ensured a measurable saving in weight. All of the TARTAR armed vessels have the missile magazine beneath the launcher, so these can only be loaded in the vertical position. Missile storage is given as 40–42 TARTAR or STANDARD medium range missiles. Three ships each of this class have been constructed for Australia and West Germany. (They differ slightly in appearance.) Initially fitted with SPS 39 radar which has now been replaced by SPS 52. A change to SPS 48 was probably not provided for.

### 6 Guided missile escorts: Brook class (DEG 1–6)

This was the first attempt to create a small costworthy AAW vessel for escorting missions. All the vessels were completed between 1966 and 1968. The Mk 22 lightweight single launcher is placed on the superstructure with the magazine beneath it.

### 50 (?) Patrol frigates

These are intended primarily to protect commercial convoys, sea control ships, replenish-

Above: DLG *Coontz* after modernisation. Note the SPS 48 antenna on the foremast and the lack of 3in guns. The ASROC launcher is fitted to this class without a reload magazine./*Official US Navy*

Left: DDG *Parsons*, a 'Forrest Sherman' class destroyer. The radar arrangement is similar to that in the 'Mitscher' class: SPS 48 antenna on the mainmast. A single SPG 51 control module is mounted on the after deckhouse, with a single ASROC launcher abreast the deckhouse./*L. Cote*

Below: USS *Tattnall* is representative of the second series of 'Charles F. Adams' class missile destroyers. She is recognisable by the SPS 40 antenna on the foremast and the Mk 13 single TARTAR launcher aft. The after stack supports an SPS 52 aerial as in the remainder of the class./*S. Terzibaschitsch*

ment groups and so on. The class will be built from the mid seventies onwards. It has been announced that the design will incorporate among others a single missile launcher in front of the bridge, capable of firing either TARTAR or HARPOON missiles. Should this large construction programme be realised it is no doubt possible that these vessels will be classified as DEG's. The SPS 49 radar will be installed as reported. The first ship is due to be delivered about 1977.

As already explained, all guided missile systems at present in service in the American Navy are mainly Surface-to-air systems. Ever since the first introduction of missiles, the Navy has been of the opinion that carrier based aircraft are the only sure defence against enemy surface warships. However, the lucky shot of a Soviet STYX missile, fired by an Egyptian patrol boat during the 1967 War sunk the Israeli destroyer *Eilath*, and a new era began in Surface-to-surface missile technology. Although some nations (among others France, Italy, Norway and Israel) immediately began to develop their own close-range Surface-to-surface missile systems, the United States has been unable to introduce such a system until now. The HARPOON system now being developed, is not expected to be ready for service until the middle of the seventies. At present it is primarily intended for installation on small missile patrol boats (hydrofoils) and on the so-called patrol frigates, some 50 of which are due to be constructed over the next decade. As the hydrofoils will obviously be completed sooner than the frigates, it is probably intended in the meantime to use the French EXOCET M 38, or French-Italian OTOMAT Surface-to-surface missile, which at present are ready for service.*

The first attempt to examine the efficiency of guided missiles on small boats was made in 1971 when the gunboat *Benicia* (PG 96) was fitted with a launcher for the TARTAR anti-radiation missile. Meanwhile this installation has been removed, and two other gun-

* For details of these missiles see *Warships & Navies 1973*.

boats have been armed in a like manner.

Just after the signing of the first SALT (Strategic Arms Limitation Treaty) the American Navy confirmed its strong intention to quickly develop a submarine based Surface-to-surface missile. It is not yet certain whether this missile will be used mainly against sea targets, or only against land targets, similar to the former REGULUS system.

What about the future of American guided missile ships? Presently only five heavy frigates are under construction, two of which are near completion. The patrol frigates mentioned above will certainly be constructed, but the exact number (50 have been envisaged) has not yet been fixed. Also the exact number of planned hydrofoil missile boats has still to be announced. Perhaps the most interesting question of all is whether the DXG programme will be realised, giving the American Navy a large number of highly sophisticated fleet escorts. It was originally envisaged that about 28 units of this class would eventually replace the older converted DDG's and the first vessels of the 'Charles F. Adams' class. It is probable, however, that far fewer than the 28 vessels will be constructed, and that they will be based on the existing design of the 'Spruance' class. But feelings are divided over these ships. The overall construction costs for one 'Spruance' class destroyer is well above $85 million, so it could turn out to be far too costly to build the new DDG. One thing is certain; each ship built in the next year is likely to turn out to be far more expensive than the equivalent vessel built during the previous year, and not only the American Navy has to face this fact.

At the same time there is also the question as to whether the American Navy possesses sufficient numbers of guided missile armed ships to carry out its tasks. In peacetime the 78 active guided missile ships of course present a proud armada, but a 'Fleet in being' should be measured against any possible enemy initial attack. Seventy eight ships spread throughout the oceans of the world where the United States can expect a concentrated attack of a large number of enemy missile carrying aircraft is certainly not sufficient to cover all eventualities.

# Naval Surface-to-Air Guided Missiles[*]

## ANTHONY J. WATTS

To obtain a true picture of the many Surface-to-air systems at present in service or under development it would be necessary to discuss many highly technical aspects, not only of the missiles themselves but also of their associated control systems and in fact of the complete weapons control system including radars, computers displays etc of each class of warship operating Surface-to-air missiles, which in an article such as this would be impossible. So that the reader may gain some idea of the capabilities of those missiles at present in service or under development I have, therefore, given a table at the end of this article from which the major functions of each missile can be compared. In addition a short paragraph on each missile gives very brief details concerning development and a basic idea of the missile guidance and control system.

## GREAT BRITAIN
### Seacat
Development of the SEACAT short-range Surface-to-air missile began in the late 1950s, one of the requirements of the system being that it should be capable of engaging low flying aircraft, which also gave the missile the ability to engage surface targets. Trials of the new weapon were undertaken aboard HMS *Decoy* in 1962. Following successful trials it was decided that the SEACAT should replace the close-range 40mm Bofors guns on the 'Leander' class frigates and 'County' class destroyers, and that in future all new warships (that is vessels of 2,500 tons and over) designed

* For further illustrations applicable to this article please see preceding article.

for the Royal Navy would incorporate the SEACAT as standard close-range A/A equipment. The standard GWS 20 and GWS 22 SEACAT fire control systems adopted by the Royal Navy have been modified from gunnery directors. These two manual systems, incorporating optical sighting and director control, will be replaced in the near future by a system using Closed Circuit TeleVision (CCTV), which will enable the aimer to be placed in a far less vulnerable position than the open director at present used. This new lightweight fire control system, allied to a new lightweight three-round launcher which has been designed, will enable corvettes, small frigates and FPBs of about 150 tons to mount the SEACAT missile.

### Seadart
Work on the development of a new long range Surface-to-air missile commenced in August 1962. The aim was to develop a missile capable of intercepting high and low altitude aircraft with speeds in excess of MACH 2, and also surface and air launched missiles which had a long range stand-off capability. This required a missile capable of area defence, and capable of dealing simultaneously with a number of targets. Thus developed the SEADART is the most advanced ship-borne weapon system in the world. It is a vastly superior weapon to the SEASLUG, which missile it replaces in the long range A/A role, equipping HMS *Bristol* and the new destroyers of the 'Sheffield' class. The great saving in weight achieved in both the missile and its launch and associated control systems enable it to be fitted to vessels of about 3,000 tons. The whole launch sequence is fully automatic with radars locating and tracking the target, feeding the resulting information via a computer to the missile, which then homes itself onto the radar reflections from the target.

### Seaslug
The long range SEASLUG Surface-to-air missile was the first missile to be designed for the Royal Navy, development commencing in the early 1950s. Towards the end of that decade trials were carried out aboard HMS *Girdleness*, and the 'County' class destroyers

88

*Above :* A four-round **SEACAT** launcher on board the New Zealand frigate *Taranaki.*/*Courtesy Short Brothers*

*Left :* **SEADART** missile on HMS *Bristol.*/*MoD, RN, Official*

*Below :* **SEASLUG** missile being fired during trials aboard HMS *Girdleness.*/*MoD, RN, Official*

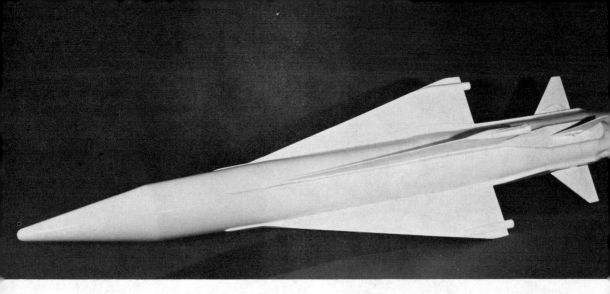

*Above:* Model of the SEAWOLF missile, which is scheduled to enter service with the Royal Navy in the mid-70's. The system can be retro-fitted in place of the SEACAT system./*Courtesy British Aircraft Corporation*

*Below:* A model of the six-barrelled, hand loaded, auto-controlled SEAWOLF missile launcher. This launcher gives the missiles complete environmental protection./*Courtesy BAC*

*Right:* The SLAM missile mounted on HM submarine *Aeneas.* Note the cluster of six launching tubes surrounding the weather-proofed TV camera./*Courtesy Vickers Ltd*

were the first and only vessels designed to carry the missile. The Mk II SEASLUG missile fitted to the four later vessels of the 'County' class has a better all round performance than the Mk I and is capable of engaging low level targets as well as high altitude aircraft. It is also capable of intercepting surface targets. The SEASLUG has a fully automatic control system with targets detected at long range by radar, which then accurately plots the height, range and bearing. A particular target is then selected and the information fed via a computer to the missile guidance and control system after which the operator fires the missile when the target is in range. The missile is then homed on to the target by the tracking radar.

### Seawolf

In June 1967 a development contract was awarded for the development of a close-range A/A point defence system with an anti-missile capability. Known as the SEAWOLF, all phases of the launch and guidance system are completely automatic with a very short reaction time and a high degree of accuracy. It is intended that the SEAWOLF will at a later date replace the SEACAT, and part of the CCTV gathering and guidance system is being developed from that now undergoing tests with the SEACAT (described above). Overall control of the system will be exercised by a development of the Ferranti 1600B computer and the missile will be fired from a multiple launcher. SEAWOLF will equip the new Type 22 frigates (for which orders should be placed during 1973), the new Through Deck Cruiser, and will probably be retro-fitted to the later 'Leander' class frigates.

### Slam

A completely new missile system developed as private venture which underwent trials aboard the submarine *Aeneas* at the end of 1972 is the SLAM. This missile, developed by Vickers Ltd, is based on the Army's BLOWPIPE missile. It is a close range weapon system being developed to equip submarines of the 'Oberon' type and also small patrol boats such as corvettes, hovercraft and FPBs, to provide close-range defence against missile

armed helicopters and small surface craft. The BLOWPIPE missile is carried on a remote control multiple launcher (six tubes) clustered round a manually controlled TV tracking and missile control system. Acquisition of the target is by search periscope or search radar on a small vessel, and guidance is by line-of-sight radio command as in the SEACAT. Other developments under consideration include a twin launcher for FPB's and a ten round launcher, which can be controlled remotely from any director, or a CCTV system.

### FRANCE
#### Murène

Design study for this A/A missile first began in 1966, as a private venture incorporating the Matra CROTALE weapon system, for use on small craft. The rocket has been specially designed for use against supersonic low-flying aircraft. Firing is accomplished from an eight round launcher and uses a Triton air and sea surveillance doppler radar. A tracking radar provides target data, all of which is fed via a computer data handling system to the radio controlled missile. In addition to the search radar an optical system is used for low level target acquisition, mainly against small surface craft of the FPB type. The rocket is fitted with an infra-red proximity fuse: the fuse consists of an infra-red cell detecting the passage of heat radiation from the target; the resulting signal from the cell is then magnified by an electronic unit the output of which initiates the firing sequence. This fuse is capable of discriminating against spurious heat radiation such as may emanate from the ground or the sun.

#### Masurca

The MASURCA long-range A/A missile defence system forms the main A/A armament of the French frigates *Duquesne* and *Suffren* and the cruiser *Colbert*. The launch system on the frigates can accommodate either of the two versions of this missile now in production – the Mod 2 or the Mod 3. The difference between the two missiles lies in the guidance system which in the Mod 2 utilises a radio command module while the Mod 3 employs semi-active radar homing. The fire control set up is based on a 3-D radar, a data extractor, two remote control indicators allied with a tracking radar for the Mod 2 and a target illuminator radar for the Mod 3, and a launch computer.

### Roland

The navalised version of the ROLAND is based on the ground-to-air all weather ROLAND II built for land forces. The naval system which is in the development stage is being adapted for use against small surface ship targets such as FPB's etc. The control system directs a number of missile launchers placed strategically around the deck of a vessel. Each launcher is a compact unit with two arms, each of which is fed by a drum containing four missiles. Target designation is achieved either by tracking radar or by optical sighting and guidance by the tracking radar or an infra-red direction finder, the resulting data being fed to the missile by radio control. The launcher is equipped with an optical tracking sight and also carries the missile radio control equipment. The turret itself is remotely controlled for use in all kinds of weather, but increased precision can be achieved in fair weather by use of the optical sight.

### ITALY
### Albatross

The ALBATROSS system has been designed to provide defence against high and low altitude aircraft and anti-ship missiles. The system, which can be fitted to vessels of any size, is capable of use in all kinds of weather. It combines Surface-to-air missiles and guns either simultaneously or independantly, providing cover for the parent vessel over a wide range. It is also capable of engaging surface targets. The system uses a SPARROW III missile modified for Surface-to-air firing by the use of folding wings and a clipped tail. The missile is fired from an eight round launcher and is controlled by a dual channel radar. Targets are selected either automatically or manually after which the complete launch sequence is carried out automatically, only one opera-

tor being required to control the whole sequence. Auxiliary detection, tracking, and target identification and control functions etc. can be carried out by optical and CCTV equipment. Development of the system commenced in 1968 and will be installed on most operational major units of the Italian Navy.

### Sea Indigo

The SEA INDIGO missile has evolved from the land missile, development commencing in 1963. The system has been designed for use on warships under 500 tons and to save space the launcher is manually loaded. However, as the system is also capable of being fitted to larger warships, provision has been made for automatic loading should this be required. One version of the system under design in Switzerland employs a dual purpose launcher and fire control system capable of directing either the SEA INDIGO or the Surface-to-surface SEA KILLER missile. SEA INDIGO is fired from a quadruple launcher and control is exercised with a Sea Hunter beam-riding guidance system. There is a standby radio control system using an infra-red camera mounted on the radar aerial in case an attempt is made to neutralise the missile by jamming the control radar.

### AMERICA
### Advanced Terrier

Initial development of the TERRIER missile commenced in 1951 and the missile entered service in 1956. The ADVANCED TERRIER is the latest in the series of TERRIER missiles to be developed for the American Navy. It has greatly improved speed and range over the earlier missiles and the new beam riding radar equipment gives the missile a far better target interception capability against supersonic low-flying aircraft, than its predecessors. The missile can also be used simultaneously against multiple targets and has in addition a Surface-to-surface capability. It is fired from a twin launcher which is automatically loaded. The ADVANCED TERRIER entered service in 1963 and its operational status can be seen from the table at the end of the preceding article,

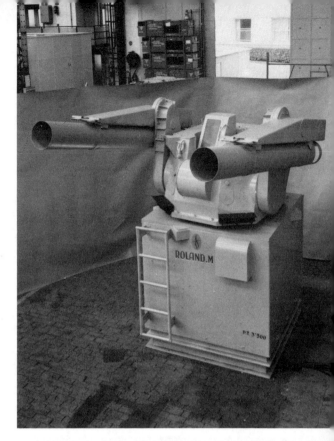

*Above:* A twin **MASURCA** launcher with missiles on board the guided missile ship *Suffren./Official French Navy*

*Above right:* **ROLAND** missile launcher./*Courtesy Aerospatiale Ltd*

*Below:* The **ALBATROSS** air defence system undergoing trials on board the Italian destroyer *Aviere.* A **SPARROW** surface-to-air missile has just been fired from the eight-round launcher./*Courtesy Selenia*

*Right:* **TERRIER** missiles on launcher with **SPG 55** control modules behind on USS *William V. Pratt./Official USN*

as can the following American Surface-to-air missiles. The long-range ADVANCED TERRIER missile also equips warships of the Dutch and Italian navies, but in the American navy is being replaced by the STANDARD missile.

## Aegis

This is the most advanced Surface-to-air naval missile at present under development in the world. It will form the main A/A defence system for the American Navy until well into the 1980s. Development of the missile began in 1964, but was delayed for a time. It has since been developed for use in area defence, providing protection for a complete task force. Initially the weapon will be fitted to the new nuclear frigates of the 'California' and 'Virginia' classes, and the 'Spruance' class destroyers. One of the most notable features of this missile system is 3-D radar which can scan 360 degrees almost simultaneously. Microwave radars will be used for target illumination with all relevant data from all radar systems being processed by a high speed computer. The twin launcher will be capable of firing either the new missile or an ASROC missile. Until final development of the missile has been achieved the system as fitted to the new frigates and destroyers will deploy the medium range STANDARD missile.

## Sea Sparrow

The SEA SPARROW, development of which began in 1964, is a close-range weapon designed to provide a Basic Point Defence Missile System (BPDMS) for use against aircraft and anti-shipping missiles. It is at present operational on a number of carriers and will gradually be fitted to other vessels which at present have no missile capability (ie carriers, amphibious warfare vessels and fleet replenishment vessels). This initial development of the BPDMS system has made use of existing hardware, but two further systems are under development, the second generation utilising a new fire control and processing systems designed specifically for BPDMS duties but firing the SEA SPARROW, and a third generation which will have an entirely new missile. The present launcher comprises an eight tube ASROC launcher modified to fire the SEA SPARROW. In the present system the fire control and target illuminating radar is manually controlled, but later versions will be fully automatic.

In Canada a slightly different version of the SEA SPARROW BPDMS is under development for use on the new '280' class destroyers and the AOR '509' class support ships. In the Canadian version the missile launcher and magazine are combined into a compact unit. When not in use the launching arm supporting four missiles, is housed within the magazine. To carry out a launch sequence this arm is extended laterally in front of the magazine. When housed the missile supports on the head of the launcher lie directly over the missile loaders, thus providing a rapid reload capability. The vessels will use two Dutch WM22 fire control systems which are dual purpose, controlling 5in guns as well as the missiles. This equipment will provide early warning against both air and surface targets simultaneously and will simultaneously control both guns and missiles against selected targets.

## Standard RIM 66A & RIM 67A

With the TARTAR and ADVANCED TERRIER becoming obsolete General Dynamics were awarded a contract to develop the STANDARD missile as a future replacement for these two missile systems. The missile employs solid state electronics and an all electric control system, thus dispensing completely with hydraulic, pneumatic and gas systems resulting in a great saving in weight and space and also easing maintenance problems. Two versions of the missile have been developed – a medium range RIM 66A and an extended range RIM 67A missile, the principle difference between the two missiles lies in the propulsion unit which in the RIM 67A has a separable booster and sustaining motor while the 66A has an integral dual thrust motor. Since 1971 destroyers and cruisers have been re-equipped with the 66A in place of the TARTAR missile while frigates have had their TERRIER missile system replaced by the 67A. The missile is capable of engaging both aircraft and missiles at both high and low altitudes, and also has a Surface-to-surface capability.

## Talos

One of the most powerful naval missiles afloat (apart that is from the ICBMs) is the TALOS, which has been developed from experiments initiated as long ago as 1944. The missile was specifically designed for very long range fleet defence against air targets, but later versions also have a Surface-to-surface capability. In this configuration the missiles are used to destroy enemy radar systems and are equipped with an anti-radiation homing head. It is intended that the AEGIS system now under development will eventually replace the TALOS, but it is expected that the TALOS will

GOA surface-to-air missile being fired from a 'Kresta' class cruiser./A. J. Watts Collection

*Above:* TALOS missiles on launcher aboard USS *Long Beach.* Note SPG 49 control gear behind missiles./*Official USN*

*Below:* A Mk 11 TARTAR twin launcher on the USS *Charles F. Adams.*/*S. Terzibaschitsch*

remain operational at least until the mid-1980s.

## Tartar

This supersonic missile was designed as the primary A/A armament for small ships such as destroyers and destroyer escorts, and as secondary battery armament aboard larger ships such as cruisers. It is similar in many ways to the TERRIER, but was designed to require the minimum of shipboard space. The rocket is capable of intercepting and destroying aircraft at over 10 miles from their specified target even though the aircraft attempts to complete evasive manoeuvres. The missile has formed the main A/A defence aboard American warships since 1961 but is now being replaced by the STANDARD missile. The TARTAR is also in service with a number of other countries including Italy, Germany and Japan.

## RUSSIA
### Goa

This missile forms the standard A/A missile armament of the Russian Navy, equipping vessels of the 'Kashin', 'Kotlin', 'Kresta' and 'Kynda' classes. The missile is fired from a roll-stabilised twin launcher that looks surprisingly like that of the American TARTAR. It was developed from the land version of the same rocket and would appear to have super-ceded any possible development of the much larger GUIDLINE missile. GOA entered service in the early 1960s.

## Guidline

This Surface-to-air missile has so far been observed on only one vessel – the 'Svlerdov' class cruiser *Dzerzhinski*. The reason that only one of these systems has so far been observed afloat may be as a result of the enormous radar guidance system associated with the missile, which precludes its equipping smaller vessels for reasons of stability. The trainable twin launcher is almost identical to the launcher for the American TERRIER mis-sile. This naval version of the Russian Army's GUIDLINE missile was the first Surface-to-air missile installation observed in the Soviet navy and may well have been fitted to the *Dzerzhinski* purely to test the feasibility of developing some of the Army's Surface-to-air missiles for naval use. It was first observed in the late 1950s.

| Missile and Country of origin | Launch Weight (lb) | Dimensions Length (oa) × Span × Body Diameter (in) | Power Unit | Guidance | Warhead + Fuse | Maximum Range (miles) |
|---|---|---|---|---|---|---|
| GREAT BRITAIN Seacat | 150 | 58 × 25½ × 7½ | 2 Stage solid fuel | Radio + visual or radar | HE with either contact or proximity | 2.2 |
| Seadart | 1210 | 171½ × ? × 16½ | Ramjet liquid fuel + solid fuel booster | Semi-active radar homing | HE with proximity fuse | 19+ |
| Seaslug | ? | 240 × 56½ × 16 | Solid fuel + 4 solid fuel boosters | Beam rider | HE + proximity fuse | ? 15+ |
| Seawolf* Slam | ? | 53 × 10¾ × 3 | Solid fuel | Radio | HE + infra-red proximity fuse | ? |
| FRANCE Murène | 176 | 113¾ × 21¼ × 5¾ | 1 stage solid fuel | Radio | HE + infra-red proximity fuse | 5.3 |
| Masurca 3 | 4585 | 338½ × 30 × 16 | 2 stage solid fuel | Semi-active radar homing | HE + proximity fuse | 31 |
| Roland | 164 | 102½ × 19¾ × 6⅓ | 2 stage solid fuel | Radio by optical aim + infra-red tracking | HE + proximity fuse | 7¼ |
| ITALY Sea Indigo | 214 | 126 × 31 × 7½ | Solid fuel | Beam rider/radio | HE + impact or infra-red proximity fuse | 6.2 |
| USA Advanced Terrier | 3000 | 320 × 20 × 16 (booster) | 2 stage solid fuel | Beam riding + semi-active radar homing | HE + proximity fuse | 20+ |
| Aegis | ? | ? | Solid fuel | Semi-active radar homing | HE | ? |
| Sea Sparrow | 450 | 144 × 40 × 8 | Solid fuel | Semi-active radar homing | HE | 8+ |
| Standard Rim 66A | 1300 | 180 × ? × 12 | Solid fuel | Semi-active radar homing | HE + impact or proximity fuse | 15 |
| Standard Rim 67A | 3000 | 304 × ? × 12 | 2 Stage solid fuel | Semi-active radar homing | HE + impact or proximity fuse | 35 |
| Talos | 7800 | 456 × 114 × 28 | Ramjet liquid fuel + solid fuel booster | Beam riding + semi-active radar homing | Either nuclear or HE + proximity fuse | 70 |
| Tartar | 1200+ | 180 × ? × 13 | Solid fuel | Semi-active radar homing | HE + impact or proximity fuse | 10+ |
| RUSSIA Goa | Approx 890 | 228 × 48 × 27 (booster) | 2 stage solid fuel | Beam riding + infra-red homing | HE | 15 |
| Guidline | 5000 | 408 × 67 × 26 (booster) | 2 stage solid fuel booster + liquid fuel main stage | Beam riding + infra-red homing | HE + contact, proximity or remote control fuse | 25 |

\* No details available.